Our Wild Winds

A Quabbin Quills Anthology

Perpetual Imagination

Boston • Northampton • New York

881 Main St #10
Fitchburg, MA 01420

info@perpetualimagination.com

Manufactured in The United States of America.

1 2 3 4 5 6 7 8 9 10

First Edition

ISBN-13: 978-1-7352576-3-1

Library of Congress Control Number in process for this title.

CONTENTS

2023 SCHOLARSHIP WINNERS

WINDS OF TIME

WINTER WINDS

AGAINST THE WIND

BLOWN AWAY

KISSES IN THE WIND

ILL WINDS

WINDS OF CHANGE

2023 SCHOLARSHIP WINNERS

1st Place Winner

GROWING UP

Skylar Winn

I remember being 11,
Wishing I was older,
So that my mother would let me out with friends.
Or when I turned 13,
And blew out my birthday candles,
Hoping that time would fly by to when I was 16,
So that I could be seen as more mature.
Or that at 16,
I prayed,
Asking for time to move quicker,
Wishing I was older,
So that I could finally be my own person.
I'm 18 now.
And I hadn't realized,
How much time I had wasted,
Wishing I was older.
Now I sit outside,
With the wind blowing
Wishing I was younger

KARMA

Skylar Winn

Karma is a funny thing.
You do good, you get good,
But why when i try so hard
it feels like the air around me
is suffocating me?
The more effort i put in
the more blood trickles down to my foot
and when i've hit rock bottom Pfft,
don't get me started on those ones that
have *forgotten.*
Maybe karma is right
Maybe i *deserve* to cry every night
i deserve ***Karma.***
Karma is me.
i am ***Karma.***

AIR

Skylar Winn

Why can't I be air?
The wind brushes over
our faces turning red.
We don't think about it
until we're dead.
To feel the harshness
of the cold breeze
tickle the surface of my skin
is such an exhilarating feeling
that we don't tend to relive.
The air blows peacefully and
freely with no end. The wind
of air is what guides me to
who I am.
The wind has no chains,
Nothing to hold it
down.
While I stand feeling tied to the ground.

2nd Place Winner

Polluted Eyes

Olly Lefsyk

Little did that child know,
that whilst through glimmering eyes of wonder
Deeply ingrained into their skin, shame stayed.
A sinful, filthy feeling of shame.
In due time, albeit years, it made its way through,
showing itself slowly.
Desperately, that child tried to hold it back.
Hiding behind walls of pain and hurt
Trying to save their childlike splendor.
But it never really left,
It was taken.
Forcefully, filthily.
Tucked away from the world that child stayed, their mind constantly storming with unknown
feelings.
A whirlwind raging in their mind
Eyes polluted by the ones who couldn't see the beauty of their childlike splendor.
Only the means to an end.
That child stays tucked away longing to be consoled.
Bathing in the grime of their guilt, eyes clouded with indignity,
Their skin engraved with filth that no amount of soap could wash away.
That child was beautiful, innocent, and sweet through it all.
Holding up a facade,
Engulfed in the painful yet rewarding process of washing their polluted eyes.
Even if that shame never leaves, it stays and oversees that child's life forever.
Their hope will not leave either, as they know.

Success Has Multiple Definitions

Olly Lefsyk

"Try again until you succeed."
Does that always mean good?
To the poet, rewriting that line
Again and again until it sounds right.
Finding solace in soft, sweet words
Things like fall days with a soft breeze.
But to that student in their room,
That student who is desperate to calm the storm in their head,
Finding solace in the idea of calm, quiet death.
Both try again in hopes for a different result.
Both hoping that this time,
It works.

Full of Emptiness

Olly Lefsyk

I am selfish,
I could have everything I want,
but nothing will fill that hole in me
The hole is infinite, the hole is never ending
Happiness, it is subjective.
wealth, success, joy
All of it is finite, they can only do so much before they lose their meaning
They cannot fill the empty that I feel.
Only the infinite can fill the infinite.
And what is infinite, anything really?
What is full enough to fill emptiness?

3rd Place Winner

The Giant and Gust

Sophia Januszewski

There was a giant woman
With beams of hayish hair.
The sun had burned and cold had blushed
Her skin which once was fair.

Her feet were bare and stepped on trees.
A dress of blue she dawned.
She would strain and gesture upwards
Then let the moon lay on her palms.

She had a wispy little dog named Gust
Who was made of wind and rain.
He ran so far away from her,
As she let him stay untrained.

He bounded through ponds and puddles,
Then he parted a wood of thistles,
And stomping heavy after him,
Through her teeth the woman whistled.

Gust played catch with suns in Fatima,
And chased his tale in Texas,
And on his way to Florida,
He jumped through a nimbostratus.

The giant women then caught up
And chased him 'round in circles.
The fierce ensuing hurricane
Quite petrified the turtles.

Then the giant and her dog laid down.
Their frantic day was through.
But Gust oft wakes and asks to play
By means of breathing breeze on you.

Honorable Mention

TEMPEST

Curly Ray

The parked car writhes under the grip of the
winds outside
us

The vehicle shudders in tandem with the brush
surrounding it Inside it is still
Inside us is a tempest.

I feel it rise in your breast when you inhale
I see it when you break our whispers with exclamations of
wonder
I hear it in your sigh while you push your head into
my chest

Collapsed into each other's grasp
The sound of storm becomes silence against
the cadence of
your
breath
still.

I AM BECOMING

Curly Ray

I am becoming the wind:
Graceful gale of joy and hope.
Every day I must sin.

Bounded by my own mind,
With pen and lyric I elope.
I am becoming the wind.

The passion that I find
Cannot sustain, only help me cope.
Every day I must sin.

The stars are all aligned.
Kismet rings my bell with his rope.
I am becoming the wind.

Pressure mounting, I'm pinned.
I acknowledge I'm a trope.
Every day I must sin.

I am not just defined,

You won't predict my lope.

I am becoming the wind
Every day I must sin.

TOGETHER

Curly Ray

Twin willows grow strong.
Together dancing through breeze,
Twin willows grow old.

Honorable Mention

Little Red Kite

Jayden Lindsay

The little red kite soars through the air like a majestic challenge
Sounding like a freight train coming right towards you
It whips through the air like an angry challenge
Sounds like a bat swinging through the air
It flies gracefully like a graceful challenge
Sounds like a whisper barely reaching your ears
It dances through the breeze like a daunting challenge
Sounds like a ballerina dancing across the stage
The little red kite spins around me like a tango dancer
Sounds like a whoosh of air flying past me

How Scary

Jayden Lindsay

How scary the wind as it's provoked by the tornado
How scary the wind as it's provoked by the hurricane
How scary the wind as it's provoked by the tropical storm
How scary the wind as it's provoked by the thunderstorm
How scary the wind as it's provoked by humans
It swirls and bashes us around
Never letting us rest

How Beautiful

Jayden Lindsay

How beautiful the trees as they bend in the wind
How beautiful the grass as it weaves and bends through the wind
How beautiful the earth when the wind tenderly strokes her
How beautiful the wind as it softly blows across the moor

How beautiful the sky, even when the clouds brought by the wind cover patches of it
How beautiful the leaves as they float and dance amongst the wind
How beautiful the sound of the chimes as the wind gently blows between them
How beautiful the birds as they soar high above with the wind at their flank
How beautiful the sky as the wind paints it a scarlet red from below
How beautiful the wind as it blows the hay far away

How beautiful the wind as it makes the mighty trees and grass bend before its power
How beautiful the wind as it blows pieces of paper away from her sorrow
How beautiful the park as a whirlwind crashes through
How beautiful the house as it is swept away during the wind storm
How beautiful the sea as it gets ruffled by the swirling, churling winds
How beautiful the ship as it gets tossed about between the sea and the wind
How beautiful the balloon as it soars up to the sky, riding on the wings of it towards the airplane
How beautiful the wind as it gently blows by as a breeze
How beautiful the wind as it whispers a sweet and somber good night

Honorable Mention

WIND POEMS

Donovan Whitaker

His Final Exit

A fictional ode to lost love

I do not need sleep.
I need him.
I need him back.
Back in my life.
Back in our bed,
which barely fit us both.
I yearn for the moment when
I may feel his supple touch
once more.
His warmth clashes with mine,
and meets
in an ecstatic hesitation of embarrassment.
May this dreary daydream shine true,
if only just for one moment.
I wait for the moment when
he may embellish my ears
with his bellowing sigh
on dark days,
his scornful bewailing
in waves of wrath,
or his cordial chuckle
that thawed frozen hearts.
But the moment never comes.
It never will again.
The memory now
brings too much pain.
It is easier to let his existence

fade from me.
Like dew at dusk,
he too must dissipate.
The sun must arise full
to sprawl across
the willing and unwilling.
We, however,
lived and loved in nights.
Nights that we flowed through
with grace and angst.
We bashed against the bright of day
and reveled in the buzzing of broken bulbs. We
liked it dark.
Now *I need* it dark.
I cannot stand light.
I cannot stand joy.
I live these saturnine waking moments
in fear,
in anguish,
and in hate,
for my light,
my one joy
was stolen from me.
His life having set down
before his true eventide.
Pushed further down
that forever horizon
of beauty and mystery.
I'd like to tell you that:
I see him
as he once was.
I'd like to tell you that:
I still see him
floating weightlessly
across the liquid moonlight,
his skin - glistening diamonds.
But I don't.
All I see now
is his devilish dead grin

holding up his spherical oceans
from which he once peered
with attentiveness and amour.
His pupil,
a ship,
which I've sailed,
enraptured by the allure of the swell,
captured by the undercurrents,
countless times before.
The oceans are now polluted,
for I watched them turn gray.
I see love no longer.
Love died that night.
Violently.
That is the only way to describe it.
He died violently,
and utterly without peace.
Bloody and broken,
without true acceptance,
only indifference.
In my mind,
it is
the most upsetting thing
in the world.
But it is *my* world.
It is *his* pain
that I now carry.
He is gone
and I get to
never forget.
To never
forget the look on his face.
To never
forget the final, "*Okay I'm ready.*"
To never
forget the finale of my man.
His final exit.
My last kiss goodbye.

The Final Wind

Before the unsettling stillness of forever

Here,
on the eve
of *all* things,
rests an unfathomable chill,
still as the infinite night,
which we fight,
to prevent the disheartening blight
of our end,
from which we peer,
imagining only what we can conceive.
On the eve
we no longer wallow
in the fact that
our spirits must dance through unfamiliar fields, and
our offspring must relish in the ashen of existence.
Events occurring with misunderstood reason blow past
our eyes
like wind on the wings of the universe,
spiraling into a self-decay,
that cripples creation.
A boulder smashed
by unimportant forces,
sending forth a tumbling pebble,
spinning through open air,
forever falling.
All who observe
bare the curse
of knowing the fate of the pebble.
When force has had its turn
and grows tired of the curious pebble,
it shall smash,
and perhaps bounce,
spawning strange new
observations. Yet, in time
the pebble will rotate no longer. No

matter how many songs we sing of
somber worshiping praise,
we remain still.
Even the most minute grains of sand
despise stationary survival.
Slowly we morph
into silent unmoving matter.
Then, eventually,
there is no longer *we* to morph.
There is tranquil rot,
on the verge of universal abandonment.
In futures of meaningless time, a
universe wiped clean
of our stain and grime,
when light no longer sails an infinite sea,
and there are no prisoners to detain, no
offenders to blame,
when all is left but the question of:
What is free?
The very basis of life
is to keep *moving*.
Tell me:
Where do we run when nowhere is all we have?
How far do we swing with no push?
Why swing forward if only to come right back? Why
must the broken revolve just to remedy those intact?
What are we without our eldest companion?
When a wind blows, will you listen?
Will you feel its lithe body drift upon you?
Will you fly away past the horizon of bleak infinite nothing?
When you yourself become
but a faint idea
blowing away
deeper into
the consciousness of creation,
an unstable wind
unsure of its direction,
lost in waves of light and sound,
abandoned by our beloved,

will you still take for granted
what once was?
What you once were?
Now and forevermore
a paranormal puff?

A Sailboat Off Winter Harbor in Maine

Sharon Harmon

WINDS OF TIME

MAPLE TREE STRANGERS

Barbara Vosburgh

Sarah knew just where to go to settle the tempest brewing inside of her. Grabbing her doll Emily, she slammed shut the front door and did the same to her car door. Before going to her favorite spot on the Quabbin, she made a quick stop at the Petersham Country Store.

"Good morning, Sarah. Coffee with a little milk and no sugar to go, right?

"Yeah. Thanks. A corn muffin too." Sarah looked at the bottles of wine, perused the selection of cheeses, and tried to concentrate on finding a gift for her cousin's birthday. However, she was in no mood to make other decisions. She just wanted her coffee and muffin.

"Here you go Sarah. Did you bring your great-grandmother's doll with you today?"

"In the car." Sarah tossed money on the counter. When she turned to leave, she ran smack dab into a stranger spilling her coffee on his shirt. "Oh no! Why were you standing so close?"

John–tall, handsome, and very mild mannered–smiled. "No problem. Never liked this shirt anyway. Let me get you another cup of coffee."

Sarah, with a frown on her chubby face, pushed her long brown hair back and gruffly snapped, "And a corn muffin too. This one is all wet!" Her Palm Beach County jacket was spattered with brown liquid. "Going to rinse this off. Just leave my coffee and muffin on the counter."

John thanked the lady, picked up his coffee, and left. After rinsing off her jacket, Sarah also returned to the counter. While picking up her fresh coffee and muffin, she asked, "Do you know him? Does he come here often?"

"You mean John? Yes, he comes every day. Lives just up the street. Probably on his way to the Quabbin."

"Oh no. I hope I don't see him there. He's very clumsy." Sarah turned around a little more slowly this time and continued her journey.

Walking from the parking area, Sarah hoped her anger and confusion would subside once she and Emily were at the water's edge–sitting quietly under the old maple tree. As she made her way, she whispered to the doll, "Do you remember this Emily? My great-grandmother found you after Lizzie's spirit told her where to dig, or so I was told anyway."

The wind was strong that day matching Sarah's mood, which only got worse when she saw someone sitting in *her* spot under *her* maple tree.

"*Hey*! You're in *my* spot! You'll have to move!"

A familiar face turned around. "Oh no! The klutz!"

"What makes this your spot? I don't see a name or a reserved sign." John said, pretending to look around.

"Well, it *is* my spot and has been for years. Find another place to put your behind."

"You must be the Queen of the Maple Tree at the Edge of the Quabbin. Very nice meeting you. I am John, and you are?"

"You are a klutz who has stolen my spot. Shoo! Go over there!" Sarah pointed to a rock about fifty feet away.

John let out a little laugh. "I like this spot too. My great-grandfather, I am told, would come here with his second wife. There is a whole story behind it, but to make you happy I will sit on the other side of this beautiful maple. I promise you won't even know I'm there." John picked up his coffee and moved to the other side.

Not very happy with his decision, Sarah settled herself under the tree clutching Emily close to her. How was she supposed to talk to Emily now? He would hear her and think she's crazy. *Maybe I am,* she thought.

Sarah felt herself calming on the inside.

She watched the water flowing over the rocks and the current floating leaves to another location. It was a peaceful time until she heard a man's voice.

"How's that muffin? They make the best muffins there. Coffee is great too. Wow! Did you see that fish jump over there?" A hand with a finger pointing sprang out from the other side of the tree.

"No, but there is a lady across the water in the trees smiling and waving at us." Sarah waved back even though she didn't want to.

"I don't see anyone," John replied. "Where?"

"By the old Elm trees, a ways back from the water."

John looked but could see no one. "All I see are the leaves blowing on the branches. Sure is windy today." He sat quietly for a few minutes staring at a small clump of grass. "Hey, I am wondering why you came here today. Do you come often? Do you always sit here?"

Sarah mumbled, "Not only clumsy, but nosy." She took a deep breath. "I told you this is my spot. That's all you need to know."

"Ok. Are you always in such a bad mood?"

"I thought you said you would be quiet, and I would not even know you are here. Clumsy, nosy, *and* a liar."

John would not be quiet. He really wanted to talk and find out who this person was. "My great-grandfather built a house that has stayed in the family for generations. I still live in it with my two dogs. It's on West Road in Petersham. Are you familiar with the town?"

Raising her head, she replied, "Yes, somewhat. I'm told my great-grandmother and her second husband lived in a house he built on West Road."

"I told you I am named after my great-grandfather John. My great-grandmother's name was Lucy. After she passed, he married a lady named Sarah."

Sarah froze. Could it be possible? No. No way. Things like this don't happen. "And why would that interest me?"

John chuckled out loud and went back to searching across the water for the lady. "What's your doll's name, and why do you bring her with you?"

Sarah wondered if she should answer. Who was this stranger? Why was he talking? Why was he asking questions? She remained silent.

"You know," John continued, "there is an old family story handed down several generations about my great-grandfather and Sarah. The story says they came here often, and this is where he proposed."

Sarah became intrigued. She had not told him her name. Maybe the lady at the store had told him. What should she do? Was he making all of this up?

"Oh really, and they had a little girl named, let's see, Emily, right?"

John came around to Sarah's side of the tree and sat several feet from her. "No, they were too old to have children, but Sarah met Lizzie here. A spirit, I am told, instructed her where to dig. They found Lizzie's doll, Emily, buried under this very tree."

Sarah looked back across the water. There stood the woman, but now she was joined by a man and a little girl. They seemed to be laughing as they waved.

"The story has been handed down in your family?"

"Yes." John responded. "There was a story written about them in an anthology once. I think it was *Cascades and Currents* published by Quabbin Quills."

"John, did the book have a cover of raging water currents cascading over huge rocks?"

"Yes. I have the book at home."

Looking into his eyes, Sarah softly said, "John, I am named after my great-grandmother. My name is Sarah. This doll is named Emily. She was found here under this very tree. My great-grandmother and her second husband, John, dug it up."

John and Sarah both stood with looks of amazement, confusion, and a trace of disbelief on their faces. Sarah found the wild wind raging inside of her being replaced by questions and swirling thoughts.

"John, could we be the great-grandchildren of Sarah and John?"

"Sarah, I believe we may be."

"You must do something to prove it. Stare across the water to the middle of the Elm trees and wave."

Puzzled, John asked, "Wave? Why?"

"My great-grandmother's gift has been handed down from generation to generation. I believe the people I see across the reservoir could be our great-grandparents and Lizzie. Please wave."

The people across the water waved back, smiled, and slowly nodded their heads as if in agreement before fading away.

Sarah knew she was right. "Nice to meet you, John. It seems our great-grandparents are amused by our meeting under *their* maple tree. Let's go back to the Petersham Country Store and have lunch, John. My treat. I think we may have a lot to talk about."

SKY WRITING

Alison Clark

Across the vibrant, clear sky
Wispy clouds draw outlines
Mirroring thoughts
Laid out for interpretation
In a way, you may not notice
Repeating over and again
Once subconscious
Look long enough
Until it becomes all you see
Not exactly written
Yet, you can read it all the same
Reminding of all things constant
And all that may change
Speaking to memories long past
As they float along hazily
Highlighting the profound
Deep importance of here and now
And casting light upon
The future which remains unseen

LEAVES

Amanda Russell

Two steps beyond childhood, they too unhook from stems,
crack against wind, walk headstrong
out a door straight into the unfamiliar woods.

If anyone had bothered to ask,
he could have said he was trying to find a way
to put the leaves back on their trees

but got lost in the process—
related more than expected
with that which regular weather breaks.
Shoe prints tracked across the house provide evidence
of the muck between dance and rest —
For a thousand arrivals, there are even more departures.

SEASON CHANGE

Amanda Russell

In the marginal sediment each season swings,
air bears its own buoyancy. The heat
rises, but cold stampedes. Gusts give sway
to the tire swing I am no longer pushing.

I stand electric at the top
of a hill, just to the left of the maple
that has grown for us
into a tether from under which we watch
as weather shifts leaves,
the furious cling to bark bare as teeth.

The maple's crown swarms and swells,
an ocean of complex viscosity.

My husband takes the kids
inside as I hold up a finger, linger to
Just-a-minute, absorb the scene, *I'll-be-right-in.*

I stand with the maple
on the verge of a rain I can smell
even though it waits
to sing to this hill
and to the maple whose roots
I will never grow into,
whose roots give height
and health to the light,
the shade, the rage of this seasonal sill.

ANSWERS IN THE WIND

Barbara Vosburgh

The wild winds we sometimes get were somehow comforting until recently. As I sat at my writing table full of plants, unfinished knitting, my computer, and cellphone, I looked out the window at the giant tulip tree. It stands over four times the height of the house and has beautiful short-lived flowers in the Spring. This day the branches, hanging low, were swaying with force, and sometimes throwing themselves onto the ground or against the house. I was startled by a memory. Bob Dylan asked how many times certain events had to happen, and he told us in the early 1960s that "…the answer my friend is blowin' in the wind." Indeed, the answers seemed to be blowing in the wild winds of time.

In the 60s we were changing from dresses to jeans, bobs of hair to long flowing locks, hats to halos of flowers, cotton to leather, saddle shoes to boots, Kingston Trio to Bob Dylan, Joni Mitchell, Simon and Garfunkel, Buffy Sainte-Marie, and more. Yes, "the times they are a-changin'." We were sure we would save the world from the wild winds of war, hate, discrimination, and politics.

While sorting through the whirlwind of memories, a branch came flying down barely missing the window. The top of it was leaning on the side of the glass. My seventy-five year-old eyes stared at the wooden object wondering just how far we had come, or how far backwards we were going to go.

Joni Mitchell sang, "I've looked at life from both sides now, from win and lose, and still somehow it's life's illusions I recall…" Yes, it is life's illusions I was recalling. A world not taxed by the wild winds of changing politics. A world not ruled by hate and discrimination. A world in which one's grandchildren will grow safely and not have to do shooter drills at school.

Nightfall was coming, and I found myself softly singing, "Hello darkness my old friend. I've come to talk with you again." This is one of my favorite songs from days gone by. "…and the people bowed and prayed to the neon god they made." It went on to say, "The words of the prophets are written on the subway walls and tenement halls…" Today, they are written all over social media and on protest signs. In the 60s, protests were for positive change. Today, there are protests for changes that the majority are against.

I closed the window curtain, shut off the computer, and turned on the news to see the events of the day: floods, Ukraine, train derailments, police shootings, hearings on the attack… all too much. So, I opted to watch reruns of Seinfeld, knowing I am no longer physically able to protest, no longer able to shout my objections, no longer able to take on a cause all by myself hoping others might join in.

I thought about that tulip tree growing so tall and strong, and how now it is losing itself branch by branch in the winds of time. I thought about the hopes and dreams we had in the 60s. I found myself wishing these wild winds blowing us backward would subside and push us forward to a safer, more loving world. I wondered if a new generation would take up the cause.

It was time to put this tired old body to bed. I fell asleep with tears falling softly on the pillow, and listening to the words of the 60s music—dreaming of a better tomorrow as I had six decades ago. The wind was still howling. The branches of the tall old tulip tree were still battering the house. I repeated the song in my head and was sad to know "The answer my friend is blowin' in the wind. The answer is blowin' in the wind."

THE TEMPEST

Diana Tamulevich

The sun glistens touching trees
leaves
gently
fall
I'm swept aside,
ruptured.
The brisk breeze rustling leaves
fronds
tumble
under
I'm falling downward,
crushed.
The wild wind whirls snowflakes
flutter
float
descend
I'm numb and cold,
broken.
A breath of spring upward swings
seeds
scatter
lightly
I am growing,
stronger.

SKY GAZING

Fred Gerhard

Swift blue sky rushing by,
or so clouds seem to show.

A blue eternally watching me,
unconcerned.

Nor do I move, small and staring
from my window,

heart sloshing salt sea
to and fro.

A breath,
another,

calm and slow,

what clouds my experience,
what deeper blue

eternity
is me.

THE GRAVEYARD

Ed Londergan

She was tired of tossing and turning. She couldn't shut her brain off; too many things flashed through her mind. Not getting a good night's sleep for the last week, she had knocked herself into the land of sweet slumber a couple of times with over-the-counter sleep remedies. However, that wasn't the quality of sleep she wanted. After staring at the ceiling for two hours, she swung her legs out and sat on the edge of the bed. She looked at the alarm clock. 1:47 a.m.

"Screw it," she said, getting up. She went to the window overlooking the graveyard. There had been no burials in a very long time. The full moon's light shone over the headstones and old cart paths. It was bright enough that she could see all the way to the stonewall at the back. Looking to the left, in the distance, she saw the peak of the church steeple over the tops of the trees. Hers was the only house in this part of town.

Looking out the window, she saw how still everything was. Not a breath of air came in through the window screen. The leaves hung flat from the branches; nothing moved.

"Why not?" she said. She pulled on a pair of jeans, a T-shirt, and sneakers, took her glasses from the dresser and put them on.

When she closed the front door and went down the steps, she realized just how light it was. The pale white light of the moon covered the graveyard like snow. She glanced up at the big, bright moon before going to the edge of the hard-packed dirt road that ran in front of the house.

The hoot of an owl broke the silence as she crossed the road. She shook her head. Who the hell goes walking in a graveyard at this time of night by themselves, she thought. Only me.

The graveyard was a comforting place for her. Her parents gave the house to her when they went into a nursing home; it's where she'd grown up. She had played in the graveyard since she was a little girl over thirty years ago. Every rock and root sticking out of the ground, each of the majestic, towering maples, oaks, and hemlocks that lined the paths as they had for over a hundred years, was familiar to her. She was convinced that she had lived before and felt she'd been here; the déjà vu was strong. Thinking of it now, she smiled at her foolishness.

She walked through the opening in the stonewall that bordered the road and down a narrow cart path. The land sloped gently down to a stream on the other side of a stonewall at the end of the path. She felt the ground under her sneakers and inhaled the fresh summer air, the sweet scent of blackberry bushes in full flower that surrounded the graveyard.

When she was halfway down the path, she saw something move out of the corner of her eye. The hairs on the back of her neck went up and she felt a chill run through her. Nothing moved as she slowly scanned the cemetery. Taking a step, she saw something coming towards her moving fast. It disappeared before it got to her. Bats flying around like that, she thought, will give you a heart attack.

She stared in that direction before resuming her stroll. Nine steps later, something large moved, blocking out the stones as it moved past them. Whatever it was, it was bigger than a coyote or a deer.

Steeling herself against whatever it may be, she turned to continue on her way. A man and a woman stood to the left side of the cart path near a family plot. He was short, thin, and looked to be around fifty. Small round glasses rested on the tip of his nose, and his gray hair stuck out in several places. The woman was rotund with black hair and a pretty face.

Our girl shrieked a high-pitched, piercing cry. "Who are you?"

"The question," the man said, "is who are you?"

"Where did you come from? No one else lives around here."

"Didn't mean to frighten you, Miss," the woman said. "It's just that we like to walk in the night too. May we accompany you?"

She did not know how to answer. Two people she had never seen here before walking around the graveyard in the wee hours of the morning?

"What's your name, Miss," the man asked, taking a well-worn pipe out of his pocket and putting it in his mouth.

"I'm Helen. Who are you?"

"Good evening, Helen. I'm Ephraim Owens. This is my wife,

Sarah."

Helen stood dumbfounded, her mouth open and eyes wide. "You can't be."

"Aye, but we are," he said in a pleasant voice.

"But you're dead."

"Well now, that's a matter to be contemplated, isn't it."

"But your stones are right there. You died in 1817," she said, pointing at Mrs. Owens. "And you died in 1828."

"We did," said Sarah.

Ephraim reached out and touched his wife's hand. "Those eleven years were a lonely time for me."

Sarah stepped toward her husband and gave him a peck on the cheek. "They were for me too."

"How can you be out here?" Helen asked.

"We don't know, but we're here every night along with everyone else," Sarah said, waving her hand in the direction of the rest of the graveyard. Helen saw a couple of others walking toward them. Several others stood near their stones and watched.

A little boy caught her attention. Something about him was familiar. He was four, maybe five years old, dressed in brown pants and a tan shirt covered by a short, faded red jacket. He wore black leather shoes on his small feet.

"What are you doing here?" she asked him. He didn't answer but turned away. "I've seen him walking the road during the daytime," she said to the small assembly. "He was chasing a small dog. I saw him playing by the stream the other day. I thought he came from the house up the road a ways. They have a bunch of kids." She cocked her head to the side and looked at him. "You shouldn't be out here at this hour."

"He's always alone, isn't he, Miss?" asked a tall, angular man with a scraggly beard who'd wandered over.

"Well, yes, now that you mention it, he is."

Mrs. Owens looked at the boy. "We found him wandering here one night. He's a special boy. He can go between worlds, the land of the dead to the land of the living."

Helen raised her eyes. "How is that possible?"

"We don't know."

"What's his name?"

"Benjamin."

"Let's walk," Mr. Owens said as he started toward the river. Helen, Sarah, Benjamin, the tall man, and a large woman with a corn cob pipe clenched between her teeth followed. The boy wandered in and around the stones.

"Who's that?" Helen asked, pointing to a figure leaning against a large headstone.

The tall man leaned down. "That's Joshua Spooner."

"What's wrong with him?"

The man's face was battered and beaten. He was staring at them.

"His wife had him killed in 1778. Nasty story, bad time."

"Yeah, especially for him," Mrs. Owens cackled.

"No one likes him," Mr. Owens says with authority.

"I don't know anyone who liked him when he was alive either," said the large woman.

Helen watched the boy playing. "Look at him."

Mrs. Owens stepped closer to her. "This isn't a proper way to raise a child, if you know what I mean. No other children to play with, just us old dead people, ghosts for all time."

Benjamin stopped running around and looked at them. Helen saw his dark hair and eyes clearly in the moonlight.

After a couple of moments, the tall man approached Helen. "Would you take him to live
with you? In the living world?"

Helen's eyes opened wide and she stood slack-jawed at the question. "Raise him? By myself?"

She felt a tug of empathy for the boy. Something else too, a twinge of maternal feeling maybe. It was a strange attachment to a boy she had seen only a couple of times. She wished the man had never asked the question.

"Well, I guess he can visit for a little bit." She reached out her hand. The boy came and placed his small, warm hand in hers. "Let's get some cookies. Would you like that? We'll be back in a little while," she said to the others. They nodded. Benjamin looked up at her and smiled. A strange stirring went through her, an unexpected fluttering feeling.

Mrs. Owens gave him a small wave of her hand. He waved back before glancing up at Helen. The radiant look he gave her almost melted her heart.

They walked toward her house. What the hell am I doing bringing a four-year-old ghost boy to my house at two a.m., at the suggestion of other ghosts, she thought. I'm losing it. Absolutely friggin' losing it.

While the boy sat at her kitchen table eating several chocolate chip cookies, she watched him. What was it about this boy that gave her a feeling she'd never known before? She shook her head.

After finishing the last cookie, Benjamin got out of the chair and stood next to the table. Helen squatted and opened her arms. He came to her and she hugged him.

"My name's Helen Martin. What's yours?"

He broke her embrace, turned, and ran out the door. She followed him as he ran across the road, little legs pumping.

She ran after him. He looked back and laughed a high, sweet laugh. He shot across a narrow footpath and passed into the dark shadow of a large maple tree. He veered to the right and crossed into the bright moonlight. It was so bright she could see the color of his jacket. Helen stopped and looked for him. He stood next to the stone of a Revolutionary War soldier, who sat on the ground watching them. The boy darted away again. He ran towards a small, rounded stone at the edge of the wall. Slightly out of breath, she walked toward him but stumbled over a rock and fell. When she looked up, the boy was gone. She dusted off her hands as she walked to the gravestone. With the bright moonlight over her shoulder, she read the inscription:

Benjamin Martin
Son of Helen Martin
Died May 1724
Aged 4 years, 3 mos.

THE DAY THE WIND ASKS TO BE FOLDED

Tricia Knoll

A lament seeps out of twilight forest,
a sigh that comes off tired and wants
to be put aside. Or inside. Beside.
Not begging for Herculean bends
of a king-size bedsheet, but bigger
turns than a swaddling blanket. My arms
go wide, embrace air and launch palms
open to the sky, ready for pleasing pleats,
gathering of creases, fly-around of hair
in a crinkle of minutes, rumpled breath
that was scattered, coiled, tucked
into my hip pocket whispering
I am here for you.

WHAT TOOK SIXTY YEARS TO LEARN

Melissa D. Burrage

I sought happiness in others
like some folks seek out cannabis,
hunting for the best dispensaries

Needing that bliss
a drink would provide—
phase two before the crash

When one feels euphoric
other worldly, when
the high is beyond compare

But we all know it doesn't last,
we can't sustain the buzz
like a country seeking oil and gas

Far from home
instead of relying on energy
from the sun and wind

Happiness, like fuel
is close at hand, with us, within us
no need to venture far to find it.

WINTER WINDS

ICE

Diane Hinckley

Glancing out the window, Diantha spied something dark: a man, looking like an earthbound crow, his black layers flapping in the icy wind. She was surprised to see the dark creature turn and head down the glistening path. She'd tried to keep the path clear of ice all winter, and had succeeded until late February, when a warm rain froze in the night. She thought that in general the ice didn't matter much. She was the only person who used the path since the Reverend Forbes caught a chill that went to his lungs, and she knew to be careful. This stranger, though, had better watch out, especially with that wild wind working to knock him off his feet.

She was pretty sure he was a stranger. She noticed he had his thumbs stuck into the straps of a knapsack, and she couldn't place him as someone from town. He must be some poor wanderer, looking for work or just a handout. She wouldn't turn him away, not on a merciless day like this, no matter how little she had to offer.

She had the door open before the man could knock. Old Mr. Rudd was dozing in his chair by the wood stove, and she didn't want him startled.

The man's face was gaunt and bearded, and he stared at her with haunted blue eyes. He removed his worn blue cap, revealing roughly cut dark brown hair. He didn't speak.

"You looking for work?" she asked. "Come in, but speak softly. I'm trying not to wake Mr. Rudd."

"Thank you, Ma'am."

"Would you like a cup of tea?"

Tea was dear, and sometimes she had to rely on the kindness of Mr. Davis at the store even to have enough for Mr. Rudd's morning cup, but this poor fellow looked chilled to the bone.

"Thank you, Ma'am. That's very kind."

"And a slice of bread and jam?" When she placed long-dead Grandma Rudd's cherished porcelain jam pot on the table, the man's joy was pathetic to behold.

"Blackberry," she said. "From the brambles out back. A

reminder that there ever was such a thing as summer."

"I used to pick blackberries for my grandmother," said the bearded man.

"I could use some help with the wood chopping," she said, "but I can't pay you in coin."

"Ma'am, I'll chop all the wood you want. Not everyone is as kind as you."

"There's only Mr. Rudd and me, and if I don't chop the wood before he notices we're running out, I catch him heading out into the cold and ice to do it himself. He isn't all that spry, and he's nearly blind."

The man looked up at her strangely, and she wondered if she'd been wise to mention that a young woman and frail old man lived alone out here on this derelict farm. Still, they had nothing worth stealing, as was probably obvious, and she supposed their poverty was a kind of protection.

She saw that the man was eyeing the photograph of a bright-eyed youth in uniform. "That was Hiram," she said. "Mr. Rudd's grandson. We were engaged to be married."

The man again turned his haunted look on her.

"Port Hudson," she said. "He died in Louisiana. Most people have heard of Gettysburg and Bull Run, but not Port Hudson. Around here, we all know about Port Hudson. Hiram's buried there. At least he's away from the ice."

"I was there," the man said. "Port Hudson."

"Hiram?" came a weak voice from the corner.

"No, Mr. Rudd. You've been dreaming. This gentleman was saying that he fought at Port Hudson."

She supposed she should offer Mr. Rudd a cup of tea, but he'd already had his morning cup, and she wanted to make the tea last as long as she could. His early morning cup meant a lot to Mr. Rudd, and she didn't want to disappoint him some morning with no cup of tea. The hens weren't laying at the moment, so she had nothing to barter with at Mr. Davis's store.

"Did you know a soldier named Hiram Rudd?" moaned the old man. "Fifty-third Massachusetts?"

Diantha lowered her eyes, sorry as always for Mr. Rudd, who'd lost everyone he held dear.

"He used to read to me in the evening," came the dreamy

voice from the corner. "*The Iliad, The Odyssey*; he loved those stories since he was a boy. He worked for Mr. Davis so he could buy his own copies and still did all his chores at home."

Diantha said, "I offered to read to Mr. Rudd from those books, but he wants only the Bible these days."

"Well," said the stranger, clutching the tea mug to warm his hands, "there's a lot of killing in *The Iliad,* and *The Odyssey* might ring hollow with a bereaved family. You know, the man coming home in the end and fixing everything, when their son or husband lies buried in a trench in Louisiana."

"Hiram was all I had," said Mr. Rudd, waking again. "Diantha here is like an angel to me. She has parents and brothers, you know, just down the road."

The less said about her family the better, thought Diantha. In a way, Mr. Rudd's house was a refuge, despite both their homes being equally poor. Being engaged to Hiram had given her an excuse to move in with his grandfather.

In truth, she had hardly known Hiram Rudd, who was older than she was and attended a different church. But the War hadn't done anything for her already slim marriage prospects. She was too thin and serious to turn a young man's head. Never knowing what to say at church socials, she'd stopped going.

Facing the life of a spinster doing endless laundry for three rough younger brothers and a pair of carping parents, and feeling bitter shame over her spinsterhood, she'd "confided" to a couple of gossips that she and Hiram had been secretly engaged and that she could not bear to see poor Mr. Rudd left all alone. When old Mrs. Whitney asked why on Earth they'd had to keep the engagement a secret, she'd said that her parents disapproved of Unitarians.

Laying it on thick, she'd trimmed her bonnet in black and splurged on black wool for a dress she wore until it practically dropped off. She'd decided that Hiram, who had from a distance seemed pleasant enough, would have forgiven her for pretending to be his intended bride, especially since she was doing her best to take care of his grandfather.

Since moving in, she'd tried to read Hiram's copy of *The Iliad,* with all its bluster and spear hurling, but abandoned it in favor of *The Odyssey.* She often thought that Mr. Rudd was like old Laertes in the story, except that Mr. Rudd's Odysseus had never returned, and Mr.

Rudd never would have a happy ending.

They'd had a hard time keeping up the farm by themselves and couldn't afford to hire anyone, so they'd sold off some animals and tried to survive on what little was left. Now, encased in ice as they were, they were approaching desperation, though they refrained from discussion of their dire situation.

Mr. Rudd slept on. He had got sleepy over the winter, and Diantha wondered how long the heartbroken old man would remain on this Earth. She supposed that if Mr. Rudd were to die, she'd have to return to her family in the too-small house down the hill.

"I should go out and chop that wood," said the bearded man.

"Hiram?" said Mr. Rudd again. "What did you say, Hiram?"

The bearded man looked into Diantha's eyes.

"Hiram Rudd," she said.

"Miss, I'm not too clear on who you are," he said. "But I'm grateful for your devotion to my grandfather."

"You survived Port Hudson."

"When I got wounded, I lay on the hot ground with the dead. Miss, the dead lay there for days in that heat, and I lay there with them. I was all mixed up and raving by the time some New Hampshire boys found me. After the War, I needed some time on my own. My grandfather was hale when I left. I guess I didn't realize how long I'd been gone."

"I'll collect my things and be on my way," said Diantha. "I apologize for the deception."

"I apologize for not coming home sooner. You stay put. I'll go out and chop some wood."

ORANGE NOVEMBER

Alison Clark

Drift away
Where the wind sails
And last leaves go
Restless
No longer home

The hue of dusk
Pulls us in closer
Capturing
In encompassing orange
Before the darkness

All fades
All prosaic
All transformed

Inevitable chill
Solid
As a rocky path
Winding beneath
Left to wander

Watch
In mysterious starlight
Direction found
It begins again
Drift away

JANUARY BEAUTY

Michael Young

January's end displays frigid beauty.
Snow-clad trees give silent witness.
Forest monarchs wear molded mantles.
Frost giants guard the woods.

Snow-clad trees give silent witness.
We traverse arctic landscape like Shackleton's crew.
Frost giants guard the woods.
Limbs litter roads and powerlines.

We traverse artic landscape like Shackleton's crew.
Home generators whir in the distance.
Limbs litter roads and powerlines.
Incessant flakes drift to the ground.

Home generators whir in the distance.
Plows prowl roads through the night.
Incessant flakes drift to the ground.
My sturdy log home is snug and warm.

MAKING PEACE WITH THE WINTER WIND

Melissa D. Burrage

Strange noises fill our ears this winter—
rhododendrons sweep against the clapboards
like the swish of a metal brush on a drum.

Rain relentlessly pelts the roof and windows
barn doors and shutters slam open, then close
as rhythmic and predictable as a metronome.

Stacked plastic chairs slide across the farmer's porch
a vent cap clacks the clapboards of an upstairs bathroom
the mouth of our fireplace chimney lets out a groan.

The power of the wind has increased in recent years
megastorms and hurricanes hammer the Cape
cold Arctic air collides with warm southern breezes.

Offering enough heat energy to detonate an atomic bomb
high tides flood parking lots, breach offshore barriers
sweep away bankings, destroy coastal homes.

We watch the wind spin ferociously from our windows
see utility wires jump up and down, an unseen child at play
notice the waves pinch together like the pleats of a drapery.

We fear another hundred-year-old-pine will fall—
its roots not deep enough to withstand the fury,
soil compromised by coastal erosion.

We listen as oak limbs snap and thud to the ground
strategize what we'll do next time to save our trees
perhaps tie them together with rope, bungee cords.

I see workers on beaches placing tall thin slats in sand
that impersonate sea grass, trying to slow down the wind
and waves, to protect the fragile shoreline.

I think of Denmark harnessing all of their precious energy
from the air. I think of giant white turbines in our ocean
and at the dump. If the wind will rage, let us make use of it.

A SEASON OF TURBULENCE

Nelson Linscott

Ten years ago, I trudged down the lonely, cold, windblown road to the IGA Downeast in a little fishing village in Maine. I had moved on November 1st from busy Kittery, away from the people I knew and loved to the seclusion of northern Maine. I didn't want my friends and family to see me suffer, and I needed to be away from enablers.

By the end of December, I was in withdrawal, going cold turkey from Methadone, a drug I had taken for seven years for severe pain. I walked up the dosage ladder to an amount that I could barely function at by an unscrupulous doctor in a pain clinic that had since been closed.

A month into withdrawal, I was reeling from the physical and mental pain. I was desperate. I either wanted Methadone, or I wanted to die. Dying seemed preferable. Unable to sleep, I suffered from restless leg syndrome, hot flashes, cold spells, severe stomach pains, nausea, and depression. Sneezing fits stalked me twenty-four hours a day. Days seemed like weeks.

On my mile walk from my rented farmhouse on Bluenose Road to the IGA, the snow began to come down harder, and the wind howled. Through the frozen windswept village, I stumbled.

I would always be considered a newcomer in the small, tight-knit fishing village. Eyes were always on me. I pulled the post office door open to go in and warm up before continuing to the grocery store. An old fisherman saw me, and though he could see I was suffering, he managed to make me feel worse.

"You live on Bluenose?"

"Yup," I muttered.

"I understand you're a drug addict. Is that true?"

"Yeah, I guess I am," I sharply answered, heading for the door and looking back at him with a look that stopped him in his tracks. I continued on.

On a whim, I decided to stop by the local public library. I had always found solace at a library when I was a boy growing up poor in

Kittery, Maine, in a dysfunctional, abusive family. So I stopped here another time and spoke to the local librarian. She was kind. I craved friendly human contact and hoped she would be working.

As I opened the door, I heard the librarian say on the phone, "Well, we can't find a Santa Claus. No, no one will volunteer. Ok, I will call back if I find one."

I walked to the counter, and she could see my need. She asked me what was wrong, and I explained my situation—then volunteered to fill in for Santa. The librarian was shocked. She hesitated, but she needed a Santa in a few hours. She accepted my offer and went out back to get the Santa suit. She handed it to me and told me to return at 6 pm.

I ambled back to Bluenose Road, never getting to the grocery store that day. I wondered out loud why I had done such a thing as volunteer to be Santa. Tears froze on my face as I began to break down. As soon as I got home, the phone rang. It was the librarian checking to see if I had made it home. She then offered me a ride to the library a few minutes before the six o'clock starting time. I took my beloved dog Baxter out and gave him his supper. I played with him and told him I'd be going out later. I tried unsuccessfully to sleep. Finally, at 5:30, I put the suit on and was ready to go. A few minutes later, my ride pulled in to take me to my gig. I was sick to my stomach, and even though it was cold and the wind still whipped, I was sweating bullets. It only took five minutes to arrive.

"You ready?" the librarian asked reluctantly.

I only moaned. At the library and up the granite stairs, we walked. I opened the door for her and followed her in. The bright lights, the warmth, and the scream of the kids almost knocked me over. To Santa's chair, I headed and took my seat. I had no sooner sat down when the first of many kids plunked himself onto my lap.

"Ho Ho Ho," I yelled over the children's happy voices.

Then the mass of excited kids proceeded to move forward with requests for every toy known to man. I felt like I would pass out, but the adults were getting me Kool-Aid and cookies, keeping me going.

Then he appeared. Standing before me was a little boy dressed in lobstering boots, a jacket, and gloves. He was dirty, very dirty. I saw immediately he was unhappy. He stood before me, and I put my hands out to pick him up. He shook his head no. I beckoned him again. He softly spoke.

"I can't sit on your lap Santa. I smell."

I reached out, reassuring him he was fine. I picked him up and set him on my lap. He was right. He reeked of bait.

"What do you want for Christmas?" I asked.

I hadn't noticed the place had grown eerily quiet. Finally, the child looked into my eyes and said, "I didn't get anything for Christmas last year, Santa. I was bad."

I had to think fast. I said, "You live close to the sea, right?" He nodded. "You aren't bad. I missed your house by mistake last year."

I could see he was believing me. I reached into my pocket, pulled out the last twenty dollars to my name, and handed it to him.

I said, "Because I forgot you last year, you can buy anything you want."

He sprang from my lap with a huge smile and ran to his father. Seeing the $20 bill, his father immediately snatched it from his son and put it in his pocket. The boy looked crushed.

I jumped from my chair, walked up to the father, and in his ear, I said, "If you don't want Santa to kick your butt all over this library, you had better give your son that money back."

He complied. I was broke but knew one little boy would get something that Christmas. I found out later that the father had been abusive to the boy for years, and a group of locals made sure he got to spend his money. They brought him presents too.

Before the night was over, I placed 103 kids on my lap. I was exhausted but happy. I struggled home through the windblown streets, still sick from withdrawal. Baxter met me at the door. I hugged him and collapsed. I knew my struggles were not over, but it was the best Christmas I ever had.

NEW ENGLAND STEEPLES

R. S. Fox

I cannot but shiver at the beauty
Of New England steeples
Too much of Miller's tragedy
Weeps from New England steeples.
Vertical, single, terribly thin
Those dark New England steeples.
Holy judgment hangs within
The thin New England steeples
'Tween wood-slat vents, a peering eye
From out New England steeples
The hating God, the hungry sky
Stares out from spindled steeples–
And how they puncture clouds like knives,
The sharp New England steeples!
And how the winter winds will cry
All o'er New England steeples!

WINTER SOLSTICE

Judith O'Connell Hoyer

Outside my window
pine boughs finger the wind
as if they are flaunting jewels,
as if they are a bevy of cabaret girls
and the pale cold sky is center stage,
as if they are doing synchronized kicks
to the applause of an audience.

It dawns on me
to bundle-up, head into the woods where
I make my way through a thicket of brambles
that snag my coat until I find the path
to the oldest house in town.

That antique place
points the way to a purple meadow's rusting tractor,
to the river that hosts a harmony of mallards
dabbling for underwater greens,
to a show of swans bowing low as if in reverie.

Suddenly,
I come face to face with the sun's sublimity.

DECEMBER

Kersti Slowik

The winter wind whispered,
"Come outside if you dare.
The ground crunches with frost
And the trees are all bare.
Step away from the fire and that mug of hot tea,
Take a walk in the snow and listen to me.
Each season's a wonder, and although it's cold,
Even winter has beautiful sights to behold.
If you stay by that fire just reading your book
You'll miss all the magic, come outside and look."

But we stayed inside because of the weather,
Reliving this year and our memories together.
Family vacations and fragrant spring days,
Lazily soaking in summer's last rays.
Homecoming and school to kick off the fall,
So many blessings, they're hard to recall.

Maybe someday we'll heed that brisk winter's wind.
But for now, we're content to curl up and stay in.
We didn't miss any magic, there's no need to roam…
All that we need is right here in our home.

THE MAGIC OF OUR THOUGHTS

Annette Ermini

"The wind is us—
it gathers and remembers all our voices,
then sends them talking and telling through the leaves and the fields."
—Truman Capote

It was cold, raw, and gray as I set forth on my walk one wintery morning. Although it was the Winter Solstice, in many ways it was an ordinary day, except I was dreary and low, much like the weather itself. It had been a challenging year—as it was for many that first year of Covid—and much of my time and energy was spent caring for my frail, elderly parents. It was taking a toll and I knew I had to adapt, adjust, and shift my mindset.

As I walked with my boots crunching in the newly fallen sleet and snow, I silently asked the universe, *How can I bring more magic into my everyday life?*

Because of the recent storm, there was little traffic on the streets to break my train of thought. I continued walking with this question swirling in my mind, whispering like an inner quest and mantra in quiet solitude.

Although my walking route is a mix of a school, a post office, and residential homes with fields and forests, I don't usually see anything out of the ordinary. However, this day became one to remember and a reminder that the universe does, indeed, work in mysterious ways.

Shortly after asking my internal question, the most profound surprise stopped me in my tracks. Right before me was a magnificent Snowy Owl! Like Harry Potter, it's my ultimate symbol of magic. I had spent decades searching far and wide to see one in its wild habitat, to no avail, until now, just a half-mile from my home.

There it was, perched on a branch, overlooking a neighbor's field. A gift from the universe, a feathery apparition, it lifted my soul like a kindred spirit. I couldn't believe my eyes or the significance of the timing. It was a cosmic wink in direct response to my personal inquiry.

Instinctively, I was drawn to it and gently inched closer. After a few still moments of observation, it gracefully flew away, gliding low in the sky with the wind at its back. As I followed its flight, we moved forward in unison, centered in perfect alignment with the road's lines as our guide. It was just the Snowy Owl and me, miraculously with no cars or other people on this well-traveled road.

We continued along as it crossed a nearby intersection. The owl paused and perched again, overlooking another field, until it gradually flew out of sight, into the distant woods. I embraced this sacred and moving encounter for as long as I could. This uncanny moment in time had filled my heart with peace, immense awe, and gratitude. This mystical connection took my breath away and left me with a deep inner knowing that all was—and would be—well.

I reflected on what began as a typical day and how it became something extraordinary. My incredible experience proved unequivocally to me that our thoughts truly have energy and a powerful ability to manifest. I literally and metaphorically experienced what I thought about just moments beforehand.

When life is challenging, I can challenge myself to find ways to think more positively, to bring positive energy into my life and the lives of others. When I take the time to become quiet and go within, I find the subtle signs of life's magic when I least expect it. The signs are literally among us, around us, above us, and in us.

MEMORIES, AS IF JANUARY'S WINTER WIND

Tricia Knoll

lifts wisps of snow to flurry
        across the new-plowed road
prevents pushing open
         a familiar door
shivers a flag
         that yesterday limply fell
sifts the snow first
        from the tiniest twigs
smears the coyote's howl
        beyond the edge of night
stiffens the chill of forgetting.

THAT THICKNESS IS FORMING

William Doreski

Today the angle of the wind
invokes broken marble sculpture
in ruins where carnivores prowl.
Distanced from the history of art,
I'm just browsing the neighborhood
with my appetite safely in check.

The last framed photographs
of the year hang askew. Smiles
of ice rim the ponds. Who remembers
the wild ginger flaunting beside
the road where old friends sauntered
days before stroke and dementia?

Who can count the migrating birds
lost in landscapes folded like tents?
I'm prowling for a dimension
thick enough to soak up ions
sparking from the cell towers
perched on the local mountains.

If I could brace myself against
such a heavy partition I'd live
a decade or two longer. My health
a private matter no whispering nurse
could touch with stainless instruments,
no clever surgeon could unearth.

Somewhere in the rattling forest
that thickness is forming. The New Year
requires its completion. My stride
imposes strings of dots and dashes
that someone could lovingly read
if lovingly literate enough.

The wind warns me I'm on my own.
The neighbors' houses look aghast—
their owners clenched against the cold
and the children too grown up to play
loudly enough to muffle
the reckless insistence of weather.

NOR'EASTER CARD TRICK

Fred Gerhard

the trees I can see from my cabin
wave boughs of fluttering maple leaves
rusty-yellow and green in gray mist bursts
gusting sideways

then up the surfacing breaths of the coming nor'easter
like a magician's fingers in motion
they draw my eyes to shuffling leaves
a card trick — pay attention now

a longer whoosh working up to a roar
for the night when it hits and the cards flip,
tumble, disappear, reappear elsewhere
in the nocturnal blink when I was not looking

maple walls bend and creak and scream from my house,
each board remembering the sway of trees,
entire forests snapped in 1860
knocking these knotholes, tightening.

and when I am cut down, toppled, naked, plain,
fitted perfectly into a groove in the earth
for all time disappeared — will I tremble
below what magic bends maples again

when nor'easters return to howl and pull
the next two hundred years?
some tremor in a rib or ankle bone
          some lift imperceptible in this chest.

the earth might sigh below a root or two,
the little gap in the planet that's me
shuffled perfectly after life is fanned out,
face up, shuffled off.

pick a card,
any card.
now,
blow on it.

where did it go?

JANUARY

Marilynn Carter

A fierce wind
bites
through layers of fabric
numbing
the skin,
clothes offer no protection.

With each step,
cold limbs
try to move faster
slowly seeking
shelter,
searching for warmth.

Spring
seems so far away.

BURN THE WINTER WIND

Melissa D. Burrage

Winter wind escapes from jealous lips,
toxic breath, man's shallow nature sips
sharp words sting, belittle and betray
victims learn to escape the noxious fray.

Avoid those who tear down, seek control
who crush debate, dismiss, destroy one's soul
insecure folks who gossip behind your back
You can do without that kind of flack.

Retreat within your own protective shell,
avoid the weather, the drama, the chill,
light a fire to that frozen bitter sky
burn unkindness, let those ugly 'friendships' die.

AGAINST THE WIND

THE WINDS OF CHANGE BLOW BOTH WAYS

Diane Kane

I cursed the wind that blew frigid across my face. If I had my way, I would have stayed in all day curled up with a good book.

But I had places to go. My doctor's appointment was at 3 p.m., but I left early to have an extra hour to browse in the bookstore near the office. I stopped to pick up a hot cup of joe at the East Boone coffee shop. I liked it the best, but I failed to remember that they closed promptly at 1 p.m. I pulled up just as they turned the open sign to closed.

I had time to spare, so I backtracked and went to Boone Center, Dunks. Its coffee wasn't as good, but it was always open. The only problem is that the drive-up window usually has a line around the building. This day was no exception.

As I pulled into a parking space, I noticed an elderly man across the street thumbing for a ride. He looked ragged; skin and bones. His tan coat hung loose, and an old worn aviator-type hat flapped in the wind. I told myself I should not give him a ride.

I got out of my car with my head down and hurried into the building. After getting my large French Vanilla, extra cream, and one sugar, I stood inside the doorway watching the man as cars whipped by. I told myself again I should not give him a ride.

I put my head down and walked toward my car. He came halfway across the road and hesitantly called to me, his words lost in the wind. Traffic zipped by both ways, and I was concerned he would get hit. I motioned for him to come to the side of the road. His face was bruised and cut, and his clothes were dirty. His cheeks sunk in around his gums when he spoke.

"Where are you going?" I asked.

"East Boone," he answered.

Not far, just a couple of miles in the direction I had just come. Some people could walk that far, but I knew he couldn't. He needed to go to the package store, he told me. Of course, he did, I thought, sipping my coffee. I considered that I would be assisting in his addiction. I even thought of telling him it wasn't good for him. I looked at my cup of caffeine, and I thought better of that. After all, I knew I was going to give him a ride.

First, I figured I would get to know him, so if he were going to try to kill me, maybe he would feel bad about it. His name was Walter, he said when I asked him. I told him my name, but I'm not sure he cared.

"What happened to your face?"

"Fell on the ice," he said, lifting his hat to show me more bruises and cuts—then pulling it back down firmly, nearly covering his eyes. Walter was a man of few words.

I asked him where he lived. He pointed to the tenement building not far down the road. I asked if he had money for the package store. I told myself I was not giving him money, and I silently cursed myself when I briefly considered how much money I had to spare in my wallet. He rummaged in his baggy jeans pocket. I heard change. He pulled out some dollar bills to show me. Not many, but I guessed it was enough.

A car pulled into the space beside me where another vehicle had pulled out. Walter seemed to know the woman who got out of the car. He called to her over the wind, but she hurried into the coffee shop without looking at him.

"I'll give you a ride," I said.

Then he asked if I could bring him back. I hesitated. I was supposed to leave there, drive a half mile, and get on the highway east. My route did not involve going beyond the highway to the package store in East Boone, and it certainly did not include returning to Boone center. I hesitated a moment longer. I was early for my appointment, so I didn't have that as an excuse. Then I remembered something—something I couldn't ignore.

I never feel good about being half-nice. I could be *not* nice; I have been many times. It doesn't seem to bother me. But when I'm half-nice, it always leaves me feeling guilty. Even though I knew it was not a good idea for a sixty-five-year-old woman like me to give a strange man a ride, I was already half in, so I had to be all in.

"Yes, I will bring you back," I said.

I got in the driver's seat and waited as he carefully lowered himself into the passenger seat—he smelled of dirt and sweat. I told him to put his seat belt on. While he struggled with the strap, the woman came out of Dunks with her coffee and tried to get into her car quickly. Walter opened his door and asked her if she could give him a ride to East Boone. She bent down and peered in at me. No, she said more to me than him; she had to get on with what she was doing.

Walter closed the door.

"How do you know the woman," I asked.

"She lives in the house next door to me." He pointed a shaky finger in that direction. "I tried," he mumbled, "so you wouldn't have to give me a ride."

"It's okay," I said.

There was no turning back now; off we went to the package store. I asked his last name. He told me, even spelled it.

"Maybe you know my sister, Carol," he said in a hoarse voice, not quite looking at me. "She graduated in '72."

I didn't. He graduated in '77, he said when I asked him. It seemed curious to me that he measured time by graduation dates. I did the math and figured he was two years younger than me. I wondered if he would think the same when I told him I graduated in '75. Then I doubted if it would matter to him.

I parked next to the entrance of the package store. It took some time for Walter to extract his frail body from the car. I watched him limp into the building. He was in the package store for quite a while. Many people went in and out. I worried that someone was bothering him. I pictured him counting his change and coming up short. I thought he would come out asking for money. He didn't. I wondered if he worried I would leave. I didn't.

He came out with a tall bag. Maybe wine? Maybe a quart of beer. I'm not sure. I watched him clutch the bag to his chest and make his way to my car. He put me in mind of other down-on-their-luck elderly men I had encountered over the years—Walter looked like them. But then, I supposed all broken old men with white stubble beards look alike.

He lowered himself back into the passenger seat with difficulty, never letting go of his package. I had to remind him again to fasten his seatbelt. Then, I pulled out of the parking lot back toward Boone Center.

"What did you do for work when you were younger," I asked, trying to keep a conversation going.

"Machinist—tool and die."

"My husband worked as a machinist for forty years," I said. "It's a very honorable profession."

He seemed to brighten as though I had wiped a cloth across a dusty window to let in the light. He told me about the places in the area where he had worked. Then, without my asking, he went on to tell me he grew up on a farm on Old Marsh Road. His father had all kinds of machinery and could rebuild anything.

"He taught me," he said almost to himself. "I got tools in my blood." I think he smiled.

I pulled up in front of his apartment. He offered me his hand, and I took it. He thanked me and wished me safe travels. I wished him well. He opened the door and had one foot on the ground when he paused, I supposed, in preparation for hoisting himself out of the car. I felt bad leaving him to himself. I wanted to give him something, but I didn't think money would help him.

Then, I'm not sure why, I said, "God is watching over you, Walter." Like an invisible lifeline, I tossed the words out.

First, he scoffed and looked away. I imagined the lifeline falling into the vast crevice between my life and his. Then I watched as he lifted his arm and grasped the handle above the door like he found support.

"Well, someone has to look after me, I suppose," he said with his head still tilted to the ground. "I might as well have the best."

We both laughed the sad kind of laugh that covers for tears.

He gathered his bag and made his way up the driveway while I watched him and wondered what winds of change take a man like him from that boy who loved to work with tools to this shadow of himself.

The smell of Walter lingered in my car all the way to my destination, but I didn't mind. I spent a half hour in the bookstore before going across the street to the doctors. The appointment went well, and I got home safely. The wind still blew with a vengeance, but I didn't feel it. It was as though a cloak enveloped me with a feeling of peace. Peace in knowing that not everything in life can be saved—but maybe if you take the time to clear the dust, you can see the light shine through, even if it's just for a moment.

I'm glad I gave Walter a ride—both ways. I've done many foolish things in my life, but that was not one of them. After all, Walter gave me far more than I gave him that day.

GRAY PROTECTION

Alison Clark

Rumpled layers
Heaped upon my shoulders
Folded in disguise
Around tattered secrets
Hold back the wind
Before it all blows away
Leaving me stark
Plain and exposed
With nothing but wisps
That remain still
Barely able
To cloud anguish

THE WIND

Allan Fournier

This is the story of one lap around the track I took in 1979 that I will *never* forget.

It was thirty-five degrees, rainy and *windy* that miserable Saturday morning. George Davis, our University of Lowell spring track coach, had cooked up the following monster of a workout: Jog 3 miles to the track as a warm-up; run a mile— that's 4 laps around the track— in 5 minutes and 20 seconds or faster; jog and walk for one measly minute to recover; and repeat that mile run and minute rest four more times.

In that *fifth* and final mile, with one lap to go, I *felt* like I had just run almost 5 hard miles.

I also felt a little *poke* in the middle of my back!

I glanced back. It was our team captain, Vinny Fleming, a guy who later that year would come from way behind to "out kick" his opponent, by literally one foot, to become an NCAA National Cross Country champion.

He could easily have been a hundred yards ahead of me. Instead, he was lurking one yard behind me. Vinny would be difficult to ignore.

With half a lap to go, I felt a *second* silent finger poke. No words were exchanged, but if we had, it might have gone something like this:

"Hi, Al ! I'm still here! How ya doin'?"

"Oh just *ducky*, thanks for asking!"

"Having trouble breathing? Legs a little heavy?"

<heavy breathing>

"So, whatcha gonna do good buddy?

Are you gonna burn the gas you *think* you have left, or are you gonna burn it *all*?

It's time to do or die."

Well, let me tell you, at that point, I felt more like *dyin'* than *doin'*! You might say I was *winded.*

I never had much of a finishing kick.

For example, back in high school, I was *ahead* in a one mile race with the finish line in sight. I sensed someone coming up on my right shoulder. It was my teammate, Billy Sullivan. He had thighs out to here...and a neck, I think! He churned his chunky legs and pumped his arms and like a bad slow-motion video, edged past me at the finish. He did this over and over, week after week, race…after excruciating race.

That makes what happened next—I'm back at that college workout now—even more amazing.

With 110 yards to go, I felt one more goading, prodding poke in the back, and I *took off*. My lactic acid-filled legs sprinted faster than they had ever gone before.

I was *flying* like the *wind*.

I don't know whether energy was being poured into me … or barriers removed.

The pure joy and exhilaration of that sprint were indescribable.

Perhaps you're thinking my story is about running hard, about striving to be your best?

If my words move you to lace on some running shoes or strap on a new goal in your life – that's great!

Perhaps you think it's about how our "peak moments" often come soon after our darkest and most painful ones?

If my words help give you the patience or the persistence to get through tough times in the future, that's great, too!

What I really want to leave you with is this:

My story is not so much about me … as it is about Vinny.

It's not so much about my legs and lungs … as it is about that finger motivating me to do something I *never* would have done on my own.

It's not so much about my wings that day … as it is about the wind beneath them. I know, it's corny, it's a cliché. I don't care.

Endurance racer and motivational speaker Robyn Benincasa said "You don't inspire your teammates by showing them how amazing you are. You inspire them by showing them how amazing they are."

Who do you know that needs a little lift, a little extra motivation? You…could be the "Vinny" to that person. Show up, pay attention, offer encouragement, poke your proverbial…or literal, finger, and look for awesome things to happen!

FREE

Mackenzie Lafreniere

How I wish I was free.
I want to run with the leaves,
No problems to see.
How could I be free?
I want love like a rose,
No care how it grows.
How could I love when I was free?
I want the wind in my hair
Nobody to care.
Just me and my leaves,
The wind at peace.
Oh how I wish I was free!

THE HUSBAND WHO WAS TO MIND THE HOUSE

Contemporary Adaptation of a Norwegian Folktale

Sharon A. Harmon

Sterling was a high-ranking corporate CEO and seemed to do well on his job. At home he was a lazy, sometimes condescending excuse for a husband who did little to help his wife Miranda. He also didn't interact that much with their fifteen-month-old toddler.

He constantly criticized Miranda on her housekeeping techniques, child-raising, cooking, and just about everything else she did.

Miranda decided she had enough of his ways. Over a delicious home-cooked meal with wine and flowers on the table, she told him that she had a chance to go do a freelance job for a day at a designing studio where she used to work before the baby came.

"It will be great pay and give me a change of scenery," she said, "not to mention that it will be a good day off for you to spend some time with the baby."

"No problem, piece of cake," he said, "two days from now that's what we'll do."

Two days later Miranda kissed the baby and Sterling goodbye and headed out the door.

"I should be back no later than five," she said, "it's a big job but should be fun and worth it."

First of all, he wanted to throw a load of laundry in before the baby woke up so he headed to the laundry room and put all the white and colored clothes in together, then he decided to throw in two detergent pods as he thought Miranda never used enough soap so he would show her how it's done. Then he went to make himself a cup of coffee but he poured too much water into the Keurig coffee maker. It spilled all over the floor. He went to get a mop but the baby woke up crying so he ran to get her and she needed to be bathed and dressed so he got her in his arms and started to fill the bathtub, when he heard his phone ring.

He ran around the living room looking for his phone, when there was a knock on the door as he answered it, it was just the UPS man with a parcel for him to sign for when their beloved housecat ran out the door across the road into the woods. The baby was starting to squirm in his arms. As he continued to look for the phone with the baby wailing he remembered the bathtub water running. He ran to the bathroom to see water pouring over the sides. When he bent to turn it off the baby's diaper heavy with poop slid off her into the tub. He stuffed a towel around her and went to the laundry room to see if the wash was done. He couldn't believe all the suds that were pouring out of the washer onto the dryer and all over the floor, not to mention the clean clothes that were folded on the laundry table.

Turning off the washing machine he noticed all the white clothes, were now pink. He was fuming and ran to put a diaper on the baby, which he got on backward.

Then he decided to feed the baby, clean up the messes, and look for the cat. Miranda would kill him if her beloved cat came home pregnant, got lost, or ended up dead. After, he would try to deal with picking up the house, starting a gourmet dinner, and trying to find fifteen minutes to spend playing with the baby.

But first, he would go up to the rooftop garden of their townhouse and water their many outdoor plants as it was getting really hot. Miranda would really be impressed when they sat for their fancy dinner as the day cooled down. He didn't want the baby up there so he left her down below. It would only take five minutes, he thought. He didn't want her to fall off the roof while he watered plants. He grabbed the watering can and left her with a toy on the floor. He was up the stairs to the rooftop in a flash and had almost finished watering when he heard the door slam behind him. A big gust of wind must have slammed it shut. This was really bad because it meant it was locked and here he was on the rooftop and he couldn't get to his baby.

Luckily, he did have his phone with him as it had rung when a telemarketer called. Sterling had found it in his favorite stuffed chair and jammed it in his pocket. He looked at the phone it was 4:30. He then called Miranda, "Hurry home!" he said, "there was a little mishap." Miranda was on her way as fast as possible. What could have happened, she wondered? When she walked in, the house was a shambles. The baby was crying, snot all over her face, toys were strewn everywhere, and the baby was half dressed. The tub was full of water with poop floating in it. The cat was nowhere to be seen. Dinner wasn't even started. There was toilet paper unraveled in a maze from room to room and toys were stuffed in the toilet. The baby had wasted no time to get into things while Sterling was away. Sterling was pounding wildly on the other side of the door to the rooftop as Miranda opened it.

THE HURRICANE

John Grey

When the hurricane hit,
nothing else mattered.
Not the arguments, not the bitterness,
not my own appalling behavior.
There were no cold shoulders,
no rude silences.
Everyone was suddenly at their best.

Trees fell.
Wires came down.
The ocean swamped the coast road.
Our house shook.
The roof threatened to lift off.

We huddled close together
without even an elbow thrown,
without a curse uttered.
We were afraid
but not at odds.

Even in the cruel tranquility
of the eye,
we had taken comfort in the calm,
as if it was somehow
a consequence of our better selves.

It would be days before
the memory faded
and we were back to our
fractious family ways.
We had weaned ourselves off harmony.
The hurricane was vindicated.

MARCH

Judith O'Connell Hoyer

March gets going in fits and starts: a sudden hot huff
coming from the heat pump in the living room,
potatoes soft and sprouting in the dark bottom
of their five-pound bag.

Now the sudden rush of violent gusts,
a found umbrella under the Camry's backseat,
potholes bubbling with loose change,
and wreaths still strapped to front doors.

March never knocks, just barges right in with salt crystals
embedded in the soles of its boots,
the sound of stamping still in the air.

The month comes on like a migraine of sirens on the hill,
cars pulled over, obediently frozen in rows
like trays of ice cubes in the freezer.

March what a drag, like watching your uncle's coin tricks.
It's yours whether you want it or not
like this week's flyer from Market Basket.

It's ice blue like the pair of crystal rosary beads
a friend left behind when she hightailed it to Florida.

March with its undiagnosed pain,
that ache in my heart should you wake
to a different version of yourself,
one that neither of us will like,
yet something we will have to get used to.

KENDALL AND THE WILD WIND

James Thibeault

Kendall stood in the middle of his backyard, brandishing his newly purchased katana. He ordered it for 150 dollars, plus shipping. This wasn't just some mall purchase; oh no, he ordered this directly from a Japanese blacksmith from Kyoto. Sure, his mom might be mad that he purchased this with her credit card, but this was a genuine katana forged from the Rising Sun—a death slicer, a piece of history capable of slicing a man in two. Kendall figured that by the time his mother saw the statement, Kendall would be an unstoppable force—which would justify the expense. He just had to practice a little bit.

He positioned the sheath in one of his jean loops and squatted low. In all the anime he studied, the warriors always leaned forward—grinning to their opponent—signaling an invitation to best their begotten blade. Of course, with all of Kendall's weight in this position, it would be quite difficult even to move, but he didn't know that—much less care. All he was focused on was the first draw—the quick release of steel in the air. Kendall wasn't concerned about how good his footwork was. All that mattered was the first strike. After all, that would be the killing blow—nothing else mattered after that.

After a deep breath, he extended his arm and tried to draw the blade. Instead of a legendary slice that could cut a raindrop in two, Kendall failed to remove it from the sheath. This caused a chain reaction: his wrist fumbled, then his arm, then his front leg, then finally his body. He fell to the ground—thankfully with his sword still sheathed.

"What you doing?" asked Kendall's little sister, Stacy.

"Practicing," Kendall said, his face still buried in the grass.

"Do ninjas fight on the ground?"

"A couple of responses are needed for that statement." Kendall listed them accordingly. "*A,* Ninjas fight on all terrains. *B,* Ninjas don't use katanas, they use ninjatos. *C,* Samurai use katanas, and that is what I'm using. Therefore …"

"You're a samurai?"

"Correct."

"I'm sorry. Do samurais fight on the ground?"

Kendall groaned. He lifted himself up, dusted the dirt from his baggy jeans, and attempted to scrub off the grass stains around his crotch.

"Samurai were trained to fight in a variety of ways. Sometimes, they fought in tall grass, on sharp rocks, and even in very close spaces."

"Wow, can you show me some tricks?"

"Stacy, they are called *kata*, not tricks."

Stacy eagerly jumped up and down. "Show me katas. Show me katas."

Kendall smirked and kissed his little sister on the forehead.

"Very well, but you need to stand back. This blade is sharp, and I don't want you to get hurt." Stacy ran all the way back to the house. "Not that far! You can come closer, like the length of mommy's car." Stacy stared at the space between her and Kendall. After a moment, she ran to her mom's car and sprawled her arms wide so one side began by the tailpipe. She spiraled three times until she reached the other side of the car with her fingertips. Then, she ran back to her brother, touched him by the leg with her arms extended, and spiraled three times backwards. Now, she was in position.

"Is this good?"

"Perfect! Now watch this killer kata."

Kendall took a deep breath, breathed out aggressively, and unsheathed his blade. He posed with the blade tipped to the sky. At that moment, Kendall finally felt powerful. For a few seconds, he no longer felt like a coward—someone who had to hide behind the dumpster until the school bus arrived. With his certifiably authentic katana in hand, he could take on the world.

"Wow, that's a cool kata."

"I didn't even do anything yet."

"Sorry. Can you do something please?"

"Um, okay." Kendall continued to pose, as though he was deep in concentration. All the anime and manga he studied always had two opponents standing motionless. Despite the stillness, both of them were poised to strike—like coiled up springs that could unleash devastating swirls of savagery with no effort.

"Did you do it?" asked Stacy.

"No, Stacy, it's called meditation. A samurai always meditates before striking."

"So you're thinking hard?"

"Yes, samurai are really hard thinkers."

"Oh. I thought there was more whippy with swords and stuff."

"There is!" he yelled. He rarely lost his temper with his sister. Even when he came home last week with bruises on his face, he didn't yell at Stacy for asking. He told her the truth: the boys beat him up after school. In return for keeping his cool, Stacy kept his secret from their parents. They had a mutual understanding, and he just broke it. Stacy's eyes began to well. "No, no, no. Don't cry. I'm sorry. Look, let me show you a kata, okay? This one is a very ancient kata, it's been passed down for generations."

"What's it called?" she asked while wiping away the tears.

"What do you mean?"

"The ancient kata?"

"It's called …" A breeze touched Kendal's face. Immediately, he thought of a badass name. "The Wild Wind."

"That sounds awesome. Do it!"

"Okay, here goes."

Kendall went back to his pose and took a deep breath. He channeled all his inner energy—also known as *qi*—and twirled his blade around in the air. He spiraled around like Stacy had done earlier, except he viciously sliced the air as he moved. After three or four pirouettes, he ended his kata by stabbing the ground with his blade. If anyone had been watching, Kendall's kata looked like an old man swatting mosquitoes with a stick. He also ruined the polish and sharpness of the blade by burying it in the dirt. However, to Stacy, it was the coolest thing she had ever seen.

"That's amazing!" Stacy spiraled around, pretending she too brandished an authentically certified katana from Kyoto. "Wild Wind! I'm the Wild Wind!"

"Great job, you're a natural." Harnessing his *qi,* he took a deep breath and pointed his blade to the sky, then he turned the blade back to himself and aimed for the point to go back into the sheath. He smiled as Stacy spun around, but he forgot to focus on the authentically sharpened blade. It did not go into the sheath but dug into his thumb instead. Kendall screamed, dropped the blade, and grasped his hand.

"Kendall, are you okay?"

Miraculously, the cut was light, but blood continued to leak out of his skin. He covered over the wound with his shirt sleeve and pressed down—trying his best to hide it from Stacy.

"I'm okay, samurai sometimes make mistakes."

"Do you want me to get Mom?"

"No, I'm okay. I just need to practice more."

"Don't worry. You'll be the best samurai soon. I know it." Stacy wrapped her arms around her knelt brother, kissed him on the forehead, and then ran off to practice her own devastating katas. She twirled and twirled with a stick in hand. "I'm Kendall," she yelled at a bush, "and I hold the power of the Wild Wind!"

SQUELCHING A SQUALL

Kathy Chaisson

A feeling in the air,
A huddle of
Unfavorable elements.
A shift in energy,
Building up,
Swirling, whirling
Untethered and aimless.
A jumbling saturation
Of unstoppable
Rising velocity
Potentially destructive.

An assemblage of
Loved ones, friends and strangers,
Standing close together
Resembling a timberline,
An orchard of tolerance
Holding firm
In the spirit of Zephyr
Against the intense gust.

Together,
Gently enveloping
The wild uprising wind
Of malevolence,
Tranquilizing the turmoil.

A calm breezes in,
Taming, embracing all.

FAMINE OF THE HUNGER MOON

Karen E. Wagner

I am ripped bare in the starkness
of this season. No leaves to cover
my nakedness or shade my eyes
against snow blindness. Again I
ignore the advice to flee south. I bleat
my struggle against the elements. More
I pity the creatures who fight to survive
these days and know some won't.

Over piles of snow and chilled winds,
Blue Jays scatter like alarmed geese
in the presence of crows. Black birds almost
too big to be crows, more like ravens but too
many of them … so they must be crows. Who
would have thought crows bully Blue Jays?
So there the nuts lay, uneaten. Surrounded
by so many empty bellies in this Hunger Moon.

The prize: most anything edible in the dead of winter.

I feed all who ask, twice daily. Toward nightfall
opossums scarf any leftovers. I could learn how
to befriend the moon from them. It might
make life more tolerable.

Hunger Moon breaks all habits and thins bones.

And now, hours later, the peanuts disappear.
Tracks in the snow tell me Blue Jays
return, salvage the nuts, take the bread crumbs too.
Anything for fuel on this single digit day.

I've felt like this before. No feathers
to scrounge in this weather
the birds puff themselves against the gusting.
This season draws their eyes narrow
their stomachs shrivel. Suffering
touches us all. The claw of winter cruel.

BLOWN AWAY

FAIRIES OF SPRING

Ellie Burton

Fairies fly through twisted mazes
of bare maple branches
and pirouette as they hit the ground dancing—
leaving gleaming white trails behind them.

More reach out
from behind their thick white blankets,
stretching their pale, green-sleeved arms
towards the sky.

Their friends join them,
flying home from the south
and rising from their dens.

The sparrows sings
and the bears thump their feet on beat
as the fairies gather and dance.
Their colors resemble mixed wild flowers
under the sun's glowing heat
as they twirl and spin.

The Spirits have awaked
as Spring draws near.

PROMETHEUS

Lauren Elise Fisher

It's the shaming of the sky
and the ground on which I lie.
There's no price to put on a labor of love,
and with that, I'll never be empty enough—
not a chance to be spared a day,
my guts and gore all on display.
When daylight has been burned through
I focus on what's noble and true.
A fire crackling on a chilly night
and the hillside filled with twinkling lights.
I could grow bitter, but instead
I'll wake and fall for man again.

YOU'VE GOT MAIL

Marilynn Carter

Feeling a shift

snowflakes fall
guided by the wind
sprinkling the earth

grass disappears
whiteness mounting
winds intensifying

an angry howl
  reverberates
    through the air

all night
winds bash
  against dwellings

finally calm
  winds silenced

phone rings
  a friendly voice
    we have your mail

wild winds have unleashed
  mailbox door
letters, bills, junk mail
  securely tied
    soared through the storm

over the river
  all together
    flying
coming to land
  safely
    upon your doorstep

Grateful for neighbor kindness

LOVING NEW ENGLAND

Tulip Chowdhury

I take my palette and paint away on the canvas with joy.
I have brushes busy filling empty spaces with vibrant colors of New England.
Here are the orange and red hues of fall and foliage
to adorn October and November.
There is brown and ash to mark the bare branches
that stare at the sky with leaves on the ground.
I dip my brushes in white to color snow over mountains and meadows,
then add green to paint fir trees awaiting the Christmas party.
Busy my brushes get when spring colors come,
there's a frenzy of red, yellow, violet, pink, and more.
I send love letters to tulips and daffodils.
I dance and sing as my canvas fills with summer hues of blue sky
I run into meadows of green dotted with white daisies.
The painter in me is forever in awe of filling the canvas with seasonal hues
never satisfied in bringing alive the colors around me.
I realize what I desire is to paint the reflection of my inner self.
The one who loves New England.

SEASONAL IN THE SARGENT CAMP WOODS

William Doreski

The maples have borne witness
so often they're tired of it.
The blowing forest recalls its past
without having to write it down.

Walking to the marsh where herons
every spring upholster their eggs
in elaborate stick and wattle,
we inhale the purest motives.

Stumps chiseled by the stitching
of beaver pose like tombstones
in memory of our mutual pasts.
The cold mineral marsh water

relinquishes not the slightest hint
of forthcoming winter events,
but offers certain reflections
some would mistake for opinions.

Have you caught the melody adrift
in the tops of drowned trees where
the nests have flourished for years?
Like humor, you get it or don't.

Have you noticed invisible pennants
flying in the flexible breeze?
Either you see them or you don't.
A cheap plastic tarp staked down

at three corners flaps like a mouth.
It's trying to swallow the dark
it casts on the textured landscape.
Campers left it for the wind to rip

into more of those useless pennants.
You discover a large plastic chest
padlocked against casual browsers.
The campers keep something real

inside, probably shovels, maybe
an axe, tent poles and pegs, a box
of nails, a saw, a bag of charcoal.
We're trampling their campground so flat

they may not recognize it.
But they'll remember their toolbox
when the scoutmaster flourishes
the key to the padlock. And then

the lid will lift and the wind-world
will rise like a massive airship
and engulf them, us, and everyone
in a single bright ecology.

SLACK LINE

Fred Gerhard

"Balance and swing," — a call for a dance,
but swaying won't get you across
the line between your birth,
and the heart of God,
if there be —

So, you wobble across the falls' hiss
trusting the Maid of the Missed
cataract visions of prophets'
mountains' mysteriousness,
in a pillar of wind

you ascend to the line you are taught to walk
singing in the strings of an Aeolian heart,
the elevation of life, the straight
and narrow escape in oblique awareness.
Don't look down if you want to rise

on this wildly spinning globe.
How steadily you wish your jointed bones to flow,
but step instead — again in wobbling wind,
arches, soles cup the slack —
take up that line. Step again.

Don't look back along the singing thread.
Step again, again, gingerly when
wind wafts sweet cedar scent
sparkling dappled brain — high.
Step,
        again.

And if angels arrive, one on each side —
from the rushing roar saying
do not be afraid
to be friend
to wind
taking your hands in theirs,
steady now,
you can do this,
trusting,

as the belly-scar itch draws you along
this accord with air, with breeze
leading straight to a tie that binds
that around which you can't see —
the tightrope's end.
You step,
step,
step.

THE QUICK FIX MISHAP

Phyllis A. Cochran

After buying our old New England home, we noticed the water pressure seemed sluggish. There wasn't much our neighbor, Charlie, couldn't fix, so my husband, Phil, talked over the situation with him.

"I had the same problem in my house," Charlie said, eager to offer advice, "The nozzle, where water enters the house, was caked with dirt. I unscrewed it, cleaned it up, and replaced it. Immediately the water pressure returned."

This sounded simple to Phil. Certainly, he could handle this task. On a Saturday afternoon, he headed for the cellar. Two flights above, I continued my weekly cleaning.

What appeared as an easy fix, changed to a whirlwind of unsettling circumstances. It started with a knock on the living room door. Our first-floor tenant greeted me. "Something is wrong with Phil. I heard him in the cellar calling you."

I raced down the two flights of stairs, threw open the cellar door and shouted, "Phil, were you calling me?"

"Yes," Phil bellowed. "Hurry, get some towels! Water is pouring in and squirting everywhere. I can't screw the nozzle back on. The threads are stripped."

Our five-year-old son, Michael, was standing next to me.

"Quick, Mike," I said. "Run up and get Daddy some towels." Obediently, he raced off.

"Maybe, you should start the sump pump," I suggested. "The concrete floor is flooding."

"I can't let go. The electrical panels are over my head. Just bring me some towels. Hurry," he hollered.

Mike returned, scurried over to his dad, and handed him a roll of paper towels.

Frustrated, Phil said, "No, not paper towels. Bath towels. I need bath towels."

This time I darted up, grabbed a bunch of bath towels, hurried back down, and handed them to Phil.

After a few minutes, Phil grumbled, "This isn't going to work and Charlie's not home."

I roamed around in search of a broom to sweep away pools of water accumulating on the concrete floor. Unable to find a broom I mounted the cellar stairs yet again and heard Phil yelling, "Call Marty Priest. Tell him to come over right away. It's an emergency."

From a distance, I did not hear Phil clearly. I wondered if he thought he was going to be electrocuted.

"Why do you want a priest?" I asked. "You're not Catholic."

My husband sounded exasperated. "I said Marty Priest, the water department supervisor."

"Okay," I hollered.

Thankfully, Marty was home when I called and he assured me he'd come right over.

I returned to the cellar to tell Phil. By now, he was drenched from head to toe and trying desperately to hold the fitting in place with towels up against the incoming pipe. He attempted to keep the water from squirting him in the face. Instead, it spurted out in all directions.

"The threads are gone. There's no way I can get this to work," Phil groaned.

"You really should get out of there," I said. "You could be electrocuted."

Phil hung on anyway until Marty Priest showed up. Immediately, Marty surveyed the problem, checked the pipes, and concluded the town water could not be turned off since the shut off valve lay beneath the sidewalk outside.

"I found this in my truck. Let's see if this will work," Marty said, stooping down with a nozzle. "There appears to be a couple of threads left on this one. This might do, if we're lucky… You can't hold onto those towels forever, Phil. You'll have to let go sometime."

Phil released his grip and water continued to shoot out. Marty began turning the new part into place. What happened next reminds me of a garden hose when you screw a spigot onto the end while water is pouring out full blast.

Water spewed forth splattering Phil and Marty before they managed to successfully finish the job.

"That should hold until Monday when the guys come, tear up the sidewalk, and replace the pipes outside," he said. "Phil, if you decide to begin a job like this in the future, will you do it on a weekday? Saturday is my day off."

FLYING DREAMS BEGIN OUTSIDE SHERRY'S LUNCHEONETTE

Shali Sanders

I am six,
Sitting in front of the soda jerk,
Nestled on a red vinyl swirling stool
Sipping sweet cherry sparkle water with Mom.

Such bees to flowers are we.
Three times weekly
Sharing this tumbler of wonder
At Sherry's luncheonette;

Oh holy corner spot,
Sacred intersection of cement streets,
Our pilgrimage to midday pleasure.
Mom embraces my little hand
Walking home: happy.

Later
In the deep center of a silent night,
Bundled in youth's warm biscuit of sleep
My childhood dreams drift to Sherry's place,
On the corner of Knapp and 'V."

Standing there,
I jump three times
Up Down
Up Down
Up Down
Up once more
No longer jumping
But flying.
I soar

Straight up
A gentle breeze guides me,
Glides me
Above Brooklyn buildings.
Surfing,
Floating
Soaring through space
Arms outstretched,
Lingering over rooftops of
Both the dreamers and the sleepless.
I know this sky from a thousand flights,
There is no time or fear here.
I am free.

My unseen wings are
A boundless treasure given
To the gravity-bound,
The grounded.

Landing as the dawn lifts
(oh soft, gentle return to the same spot
again and again and again...)
I am awakened by
Muffled morning household motions,
Knowing,
At so young an age
We are all such full stories
Beyond the face and
Shape of us.

We are all
Such elegant and
Boundless travelers
Just as the
Masters once portrayed us.

A WHIRLING WIND OF SUCH HOT AIR

Steven Michaels

A whirling wind of such hot air
comes whistling waspishly from my lips:
the only thing to stop it is my foot.
Instantly I suck
on the big toe of regret
wishing my words would wind back
into my unmuted maw.
Nothing prepares me for the torrid tornado
issuing forth from my mouth.
Her exit is abrupt,
like air escaping a room.
Doors slamming,
Walls trembling,
the only things left
of her presence.
In the wake of this wordy windstorm
our house becomes a windswept wasteland.
My sorrowful sorry sorely echoes
down a lonely hallway:
so stands a gassy bellows from a broken man
whose bleating is as boorish as anything with horns.
Later I'll convince myself
that my thunderous reproach
was meant to keep her
from taking the wind out of my sails
never really realizing
how much I need her
navigation
and how without her
I won't have any air
at all.

HOUR OF THE OWL

Steven Michaels

Deadly assassin of the night sky
I hear your warrior's cry
Which sends field mice scurrying
With each screeching echoey surprise.

Pity the poor rodent
Who trembles at your call
And stumbles from its hovel
To become a victim of the fall.

Talons raking cool night air
Descend upon the victim
Who dared to sniff the rotting leaves:
From this, I gain some wisdom.

IN IRONS

David Story Allen

Joe Slocum was one of those people whose path through life was seemingly too busy to be bothered with email. A sailing pal and college roommate of Gordon Lowes, he seemed to have disappeared somewhere in Europe a few months ago until his missive showed up in Gordon's inbox one almost gray Saturday afternoon.

Gordo-
The EU is a mess, but the UK is fun. Landed a teaching job at Trinity School in Devon - Teignmouth is the local hotspot. Donald Crowhurst's notion of sailing around the world from here in the '60s is the local claim to fame. A regional soccer team is celebrated at local pubs, and that fills my evenings. Was being a colony of this country so bad? More later.
Best – Sloke

He had attached an image to the message, a rumpled middle-aged fellow with dark hair gnarled by sea air, a Hemingway mustache and small unknowable eyes. Donald Crowhurst. Less than a minute of research conveyed that he'd set out from Teignmouth to circumnavigate the globe in 1968 but vanished somewhere in the Atlantic. This last factor nudged Gordon to glance out the window, which afforded the light of a fifty degree fall day under a milky sky. Having a book on reserve at the Charlestown branch of the Boston Public Library was one more reason to head that way and see about grabbing some wind before November made doing so out of the question.

Traffic from the backside of Beacon Hill to Charlestown is seldom a problem, and this is especially so on a Saturday afternoon. A hardscrabble jumble of brick housing projects and wooden three-deckers on the northern edge of Boston, Charlestown is a stalwart blue color enclave that's constantly staring gentrification in the face, convinced that there was something noble in urban squalor and a paucity of off-street parking. Nevertheless, you could moor a boat off it for a fraction of what it would cost you in Boston Harbor proper.

Gordon swung by the library, left the book in his car and asked the dockmaster on duty to run him out to his boat, which was a mere three hundred feet off the dock.

"Today?" the dockmaster muttered, without looking up from his copy of the Boston Herald. "Really?" The fellow in the poly-blend Bruins ski cap was incredulous. "I can't believe you haven't pulled your boat yet. Next week is Halloween f'chrissake."

Gordon refrained from commenting on the man's superior calendar skills. "Yeah, but look at this," he raised his palm towards the sky. "We might not see fifty degrees again until April. Gotta grab this weather while you can."

The Bruins fan rolled his eyes, wrenched himself from a stool and meandered towards the dinghy at the end of the dock. Running Gordo out to his boat, they both eyed the lonely mooring balls bobbing in the dark, greasy water. Most owners had already pulled their boats for the winter, but work and three straight weekends out of town had kept Gordon from doing so in September, so grabbing one last bit of wind before pulling it was in order.

Slowing as the dingy approached Gordon's Rhodes 19', the dockmaster waited until his passenger had climbed aboard his craft, then turned the outboard so as to pull away. "I'll be here until five p.m. After that..." He cocked his head in a not-my-problem-after-that sort of way, and headed back to the dock.

Raising the jib first, then the main and untying from his mooring, he allowed the wind to fill his sails and soon he was heeling to port and then starboard as he tacked out towards the greater harbor. Some sudden puffs of wind got his attention, but that was why he was there. He hauled in his sails and hiked out onto his port gunwale.

Looking over his shoulder, he found his attention drawn to Boston's waterfront, wondering where a wind from the west was coming from, since the entire vista that way was a wall of brick and glass, nothing but city. Staying ahead of the wind, and whatever the wind has in mind, is an engaging enough endeavor that sunlight and temperature can change so quickly that someone who's just watching his sails might not notice their shifts.

Gordon cast his eyes skyward, and his brow slowly wrinkled. *Where the hell did this come from?* Gazing out over the water's surface, he suddenly found white caps flicking their tongues out at him, then disappearing back into the dark green wash. Late in the afternoon, wind usually does one of two things – either quiets down to the point that you can be going nowhere on flat water, or kicks up as if awoken and angry after slumbering all day. A case of the latter was at hand. A gust tugged his bow to port in a jolting motion, prompting Gordon to reflexively uncleat his mainsail. Doing so released it, allowing the wind at hand to work its will and otherwise pass him by, rather than be at the mercy of sail responding to nature, and doing what physics would dictate. If one is racing and can grab some gusts just right, it can make all the difference. But wind, water, and nature in general can be fickle. Without knowing how it came about, Gordo found himself sailing ahead of a steady stiff wind.

There is the adage that if you don't like the weather in New England, just wait five minutes, and it will change. Gone now were the Indian Summer hues and retiring swells of when he arrived at the dock. A jibe could head him towards the container ship docks and a bit of shelter.

Jibing is turning a boat when the wind is at one's stern, which allows you to stay on course without losing speed. Depending how good one is at the maneuver, it can involve the mainsail whipping around like a screen door in a hurricane unless it is hauled in tightly and the tiller is used to bring the boat around gently.

Gordon knew the drill, and squinted over his shoulder into the wind, trying to pick the right moment to jibe. As he did, it occurred to him that the gentle splashes on his face were not from white caps but were raindrops being blown horizontally. *What the...*Over the bow, the jib began luffing, getting played by the wind with such abandon that he glared at the sheet in his hand, the rope controlling the jib, considering his options as an uneasy concern rose within him. If I tighten it, there could be more wind than I want, but if I let it out...This second choice seemed a very un-Ted Turner-esque thing to do.

Shortly, he was relieved of the decision. A gust filled the jib and yanked the sheet from his hand with a force such that resistance seemed useless. Fine. Take it. Just let me get aground in this crap. Just, please: my bow into the wind. The point of least resistance with a vessel, if the bow is pointed in the wind, there is virtually no surface area for wind to have at the sails. Being 'in irons,' as the term suggests, means not going anywhere, which right now seemed best.

Managing his mainsail and tiller, Gordo brought the bow around to port, towards his left side. Like riding a bicycle with no hands or killing a mosquito, turning a boat in such a blow must be done quickly to be done at all. As if it was waiting for Gordon to begin this maneuver, like an invisible wall, the gale's greatest gust came off the surface and slammed into him. As the mainsail swung out towards starboard, he loosened his hold on the sheet, dumping all the wind he could. He came to port some more and pointed his bow toward Spectacle Island, perhaps chewing on the notion of putting in there and waiting for things to calm. The steady wind from the west made getting there easy, but as he neared the DNR dock, a stronger puff from his stern forced a jibe, sending him away from his intended haven.

He'd have to try and come about and head for the dock into the wind. Everything about him, however, seemed indifferent to his intent. It was as if downtown Boston was exhaling to the east, and he was weathering its blasts. Ceding to the change in direction, he came around even more to make for Long Wharf of the Seaport District, but looking up at his telltales, he noticed that those small strands of cloth on his stays that told him the wind's direction were stretched out straight to the east. It is one thing to paddle upstream, but another to swim up a waterfall. While he hadn't been looking, the milky sky had turned to a lower, gray ceiling. Given the docile morning, with sunlight flirting about, he hadn't bothered to check the forecast before heading out. As another gust kicked up, that he had settled for a Red Sox cap and old sweatshirt for this venture was another cause to grind his teeth.

Usually one can count on the odd power boater heading in from Georges or Peddocks Island around this time of day, but apparently such folks had checked the marine forecast, or had run out of beer a few hours earlier. Somehow on a late October afternoon, he seemed to have Boston Harbor to himself.

Nix's Mate came into view. A pyramid marker on a dangerous shoal in the outer harbor, it was easy to avoid, but deep down, perhaps Gordon was wishing that it had retained its topography of two centuries ago, when it was a land mass large enough to graze animals on. With a kick up centerboard, he'd run aground and…do what? There didn't seem to be anyone else on the water to hail. The logic of this now seemed clear: somehow things had gone from October on an inland lake to November on Lake Superior in less than half an hour.

Beyond the shoal that Nix's warned of was Gallop's Island, then…Portugal? Gordon considered dropping his sail a bit, a nautical signal of distress. In spite of the logic of doing so, it was also an undeniable admission of poor seamanship, conceding that the sea had clearly bested him. Pride gave him pause for a few seconds until the hum of an engine cut the air. A hundred yards off his bow, a Boston Whaler was headed his way from further out. He could make out the figure of a man at the wheel and in keeping the nautical etiquette, they exchanged waves. As the whaler neared and downshifted, Gordon came about, basically turning around in place and while unable to sail into the wind, with his bow in that direction he was now 'in irons,' such that he proceeded to bob in place with his mainsail in so tight that the wind pulled him neither one way or the other.

"Hi there," Gordon offered, with a knowing look that he hoped didn't convey too much need. The fellow at the wheel waved again. His dark mop of hair was uncovered in spite of the weather and his pale skin suggested not much time on the water lately. A full mustache concealed whether he was smiling or frowning. The awkward silence prodded Gordon to speak again.

"Dirty weather." A slight nod was offered in response. "Didn't see it coming."

As both crafts bobbed and rocked on the dark green sea, a quiet from the city and airport seemed to spread about them. The fellow in the whaler turned to his gear and came up with a coil of rope. The sight of it forced a grateful smile from Gordon.

The whaler's engine was killed, and its owner climbed onto Gordon's boat, feeding one end of the rope through the eye hook on the bow. Looking at his face, Gordon cocked his head. He had seen this face before…recently, but he couldn't recall where. It was a familiar face to which he couldn't attach an experience or encounter. Gordon watched him run it through the eye hook twice, then go back to his stern to tie both ends there. Turning to Gordon, the silent figure nodded, started his engine and after giving himself some distance from the sailboat, turned around so that he was pointed out to sea. This baffled Gordon for a second, but he was so grateful to a tow that he wasn't about to start giving directions.

"Can't tell you what this means!" he called so as to be heard over the engine. "I'm really in your debt."

Without turning around, his rescuer gave a 'no problem' back of his hand wave. The engine grew louder, and as the rope became taut, Gordon was on the move. After a few moments, his face betrayed some confusion; it seemed safe to turn and head in, but they were still headed away from shore.

"My name's Gordon by the way," he called over the engine and the increasing wake between their crafts. His savior simply nodded. "You are?" he added, fishing for his name.

They picked up speed, and the shores and extensions of the city receded, replaced with the dark green sea and the failing afternoon overhead. Something beyond a chill overtook Gordon.

"Excuse me!" he shouted into the wind, which he now felt, owing to their speed towards the greater North Atlantic, "Where are we…Hey, what's your name?!?!"

The engine of the whaler quieted for a moment, and the boat slowed, allowing the tow line to slack, and Gordon's boat edged closer. It seemed as though the day was failing faster now. At the wheel of the whaler, its captain turned towards Gordon without expression and answered.

"Donald."

KISSES IN THE WIND

PINWHEELS (A TRUE STORY)

Chele Pedersen Smith

Eight curled triangles met in the middle. Fastened by a pin on a stick, the plastic wheel whirled. Charmel stared in awe at the blurring roulette, colorful and sparkly, as the breeze twirled the twists to her fascination.

My half-sibling, Charmel, who has always felt like a whole, is twelve years younger than me. While my brother and I were Navy brats, she grew up with our Dad in their Connecticut town, and pinwheels were their thing. Just like their weekly McDonald's Happy Meals, he'd often buy her a spinning whirligig of wow. So, it was only fitting in 2002, that she pushed pinwheels into the dirt around Dad's grave.

Cherished from childhood, these little novelties provided more than just nostalgia. The metallic petals festooned the place as Pop waited for his marker. Each time we visited, we couldn't believe he was gone. We missed him so much! Our groovy musician/artist/daddio was, for us, our unconditional love and a creative, kindred spirit. But for my sister, he was also her closest friend and confidante.

At the cemetery, Char took solace in their secret sit-ins. Fenced in by pinwheels glinting in the sun, my sister softly poured her heart out to Dad. Sometimes her planted spirals swirled in response! When that happened, Charmel glanced around, but there was never any wind — not even a light breeze. She felt especially comforted on those days.

BARDS

Barbara Vosburgh

A wild tempest was blowing outside.
As I closed my eyes, I wanted to hide.
But a wonderful dream I had that night,
Of a table lit by soft candlelight.

In the pale light, I saw faces of bards.
Shelley, Keats, and Frost were acting like guards.
Kipling, MacNeice, and Yeats were all there too.
From tankards we drank, a brown tasteful brew.

Our plates full of taters, veggies, and meats.
Our bottoms planted on old wooden seats.
"What say you to us, Dear Lady Bard?"
I knew what I'd say would catch them off guard.

"Your rules are all broken, shattered, and bent.
I don't know where or why they all went."
I wept as I told them of free flowing verse.
Their not understanding made it all worse.

"No longer do I need to write in rhymes.
It's a thing of the past, gone with the times."
"What's that you say, oh Bard of today?
This is not true. No. No, we all say."

"Alas my Dear Bards, true words do I speak."
As I gave them a book, "Just take a peek."
Their mouths opened wide, shattered, confused.
They stood from their seats. Not all seemed amused.

All bid me farewell with faces like stone,
And soon I was left at the table alone.
What have I done? Will I see them again?
I started to weep; picked up my pen.

My favorite bards of so long ago,
Gone in a flash as I awoke with woe.
The winds in my mind are all quiet now.
Outside they howl, still battering my brow.

The winds may subside, and I hope and pray
That my dream stay with me both night and day.
I know not when tempest winds will return
With my hope for my bards for whom I yearn.

SOUL OF THE MEKONG

Lorri Ventura

The Mekong River hums
Happy to host the morning's floating market
A woman stands tall
In her dilapidated sampan
Sun's rays dance
Atop her non la hat
Wisps of gray hair wave beneath its cone
She poles deftly
Through a cluster of similar vessels
None look water-worthy
Yet all bob jauntily
Their bows decorated with brightly colored eyeballs
Painted there to ensure a safe homecoming
The woman's sampan groans
With the weight of baskets made from water hyacinths
Overflowing with freshly-harvested rambutans—
Red, eyelashed fruits
Vietnamese treasures
Nearby, a boy sits in a sampan laden with chilies and bananas
And a family offers pimply-skinned guavas from a vessel
That wobbles, low and heavy in the river
All nod respectfully as the old woman glides past
She greets no one
Yet blesses everyone she passes
Her skin as silt-colored as the river she commands
The soul of the Mekong shines through her eyes

HOTEL COSTES

Mary Anne Kalonas Slack

Marina waited outside the clothing boutique, her eyes scanning the street for a café where she could have a coffee, slip a book out of her bag, and read. She'd have to let Angie know where she was, of course. For all of her friend's strong opinions and nonstop chatter, she knew Angie was nervous about being alone on the streets of Paris.

The trip had been Angie's idea, proposed one winter day on a hike around the lake near Angie's new condo. Bill had been gone for three years and Angie had sold her house, packed up the remains of their life together, and disbursed it to her four children. Angie had always wanted to go to Paris and had tried to persuade Bill many times, but the furthest they'd traveled was to Las Vegas—close enough for him to see the Eiffel Tower without getting a passport. Now she was alone with a comfortable income, thanks to Bill's excellent money management. Angie wanted to go to places she'd always dreamed about: Paris first, and if that went well, London, Dublin, and Rome.

After all, life was short and could be snuffed out in a second, as she and Marina both knew very well. Angie's Bill had suffered a massive heart attack while raking leaves on a beautiful November day and died right there on their front lawn. Just a year later, Marina opened her door to two state troopers who told her that Jeff, her husband of twenty years and the father of her three stepchildren, had been killed in a crash on the Mass Pike. A late November snow squall had blown through, blinding drivers and causing a twenty-car pileup.

That was two years ago. Marina, who'd traveled extensively with Jeff in their years together, hadn't been anywhere since his death. She loved Paris, spoke French fluently, and thought that showing her old friend around might be just what she needed to get herself traveling again. But Angie wanted to shop, returning to their hotel each day with bags full of gifts for her children and grandchildren. Marina wanted to read in French, sip coffee in cafés while she watched people go by, look at paintings at the Musée d'Orsay and think about her life with Jeff. But perhaps it was time to think about her life without him.

The women had met in kindergarten and were best friends throughout their school years. Angie had gotten married the fall after their high school graduation, and Marina came home from college to be her maid of honor. They grew apart as college life, followed by Marina's teaching career, led the two women on different paths. They saw each other occasionally until Marina met and married Jeff when she was thirty-nine, and became a stepmother to his three young children; then she called Angie frequently for advice.

But that was all behind them now. They were sixty-one and their kids were grown. Angie's kids had families of their own. The women were widows, trying to find their place in the world.

Marina found a café after walking a few blocks. She ordered coffee and texted Angie directions. People passed by on the sidewalk—tourists in comfortable shoes and sun hats, well-dressed women in tight jeans and stiletto heels, young, slender dog walkers with three or four creatures on leashes. Marina had enjoyed cafés on her frequent trips to Europe for many years, either with Jeff at her side or just a text or call away. Whenever she spotted something that interested her or made her laugh, her hand would automatically reach for her phone. It took her several seconds to remember that he would not respond. The finality of that still took her breath away before the sadness flooded through her. She wondered if that would ever go away.

She spotted Angie making her way down the street, anxiously looking for her. Marina stood up and waved. Her friend's relief was visible as she smiled and joined her at the small table.

"I hardly recognized you. You look like a real *Parisienne* sitting there." A waiter asked Angie if she would like anything.

"What are you having?" she asked Marina

"*Café au lait.*"

Angie looked at her watch. "I suppose it's too early for wine. *Café au lait* it is, *s'il vous plait.*"

Marina noticed that Angie wasn't carrying a shopping bag for once. "No luck in the boutique?"

"No, but I learned something interesting." She leaned across the table toward her friend. "There was very intriguing music playing, sort of Turkish-sounding but with a modern beat. I looked up on my phone how to say, 'I like this music' in French. The salesgirl was very nice—they're not always nice in these shops—sometimes they're very snooty, but this one smiled and told me the music was from Hotel Costes. She told me all about it and we have to go there. Have you ever been?"

Marina shook her head.

"Well, I think we should go tonight, just for one drink. We can get all dressed up. It's probably wildly expensive, but I'm sure we can afford one drink."

"What's so special about it?"

"The girl said it's '*très sensuelle.*' It smells wonderful, she said, and everything is lit by candles and decorated in red velvet."

It sounded a little tacky to Marina, but tacky in Paris was a far cry from tacky in Albany, New York, where they lived. Marina agreed to indulge her friend, but first insisted they visit the Picasso Museum in the Marais. They had a late lunch at a little bistro near their hotel and went back to rest until Angie deemed it an appropriate time to head to the hotel. They couldn't go before eight-thirty, otherwise they'd look like a couple of tourists.

"Aren't we, though?" Marina asked.

"As long as you do the talking, in French, and I just smile and nod my head, no one needs to know that."

Marina laughed.

They took a taxi to the Place Vendôme and walked a short distance to the hotel. Every aspect of it was exquisite—the ceilings painted a deep red, the woodwork dark and ornate. And just as the salesgirl had told Angie, *très sensuelle*, with slightly exotic music weaving its own spell.

The two women found their way to the bar and headed for a table, but suddenly that felt too painfully intimate to Marina. She wanted to be there with her husband and, knowing it couldn't be so, squeezed her friend's arm. At nine o'clock it was not very crowded and they found two empty stools at the long bar. Marina spoke in French to the bartender and he responded in kind. He recommended their signature cocktails, and she ordered mojitos without asking Angie. After all, she wanted to pretend to be French tonight. Let her have her harmless deception if it made her happy.

When the bartender had stepped away Angie whispered, "I'm paying for these."

"Okay, *merci*,"

"Have you ever seen a more romantic setting in your life? It's perfect for a marriage proposal. Oh, to be young again. What was I thinking, getting married at eighteen and spending vacations in the Finger Lakes or the Catskills when I could have been in Paris? What a fool I was." Angie stopped speaking as their drinks arrived, beverages as beautiful as the room itself. She took a first sip. "Oh my God, I could live like this for the rest of my life."

"You'd run out of money, Angie. But you can still live well and have adventures—"

"*Excusez-moi, Mesdames.*" They turned to see a tall, dark-haired man with a well-trimmed, graying beard standing behind them. He wore a silk shirt under a black sports jacket with a paisley silk handkerchief in the breast pocket. "You are American?" His accent was French.

"Oui!" Angie answered with a friendly smile.

Marina only glanced at him and took a sip of her cocktail.

"*Mon amie parle Françaistrès bien*," Angie told the man, tapping lightly on Marina's arm.

"Ah," he said with a polite smile. "I speak English. My friend and I would be honored if you would join us at our table." He indicated a table across the room where the friend nodded and smiled.

"Oh, *merci*. How nice." Angie looked at Marina, who seemed fascinated with her cocktail napkin. "Can you give us a few moments, please?"

"*Certainement*." His voice was a rumbling, sexy baritone. "Join us when you're ready."

"Marina, this is no time to be a stick-in-the-mud. You were just saying I should have adventures and poof—this handsome creature invites us to join him. What's the matter with you?"

Her friend took a deep breath and exhaled with a sigh. "Angie, I didn't come out tonight to get picked up in an overpriced hotel bar."

"Neither did I. And really Marina, it's not like we're going to sleep with them, for heaven's sake. We'll just have one drink and then say goodnight."

"I'm not sure it works that way, Angie."

"Oh, come on. What are you afraid of?"

"I'm just not ready for this. I've been on the verge of tears since we walked in here. I want to be at one of those romantic, candlelit tables with my husband. I don't want to make small talk with strange men."

"Oh, honey. I'm sorry, I didn't realize. You used to do these sorts of things with Jeff. Of course it's hard. I never did anything remotely similar with Bill, so, it doesn't hurt. Going to the hardware store hurts, picking up my grandkids at the bowling alley hurts. But this, this feels good."

Marina's eyes glistened with tears, but she couldn't help but chuckle. She dabbed her eyes with her napkin. "Okay, one drink. But don't get carried away or flirt brazenly with these men. And after one drink we tell them we have to go. If you want anything more, give him your cellphone number, but keep me out of it. I'll be civil, but I won't be charming."

Angie nodded and turned to lead the way to a dim corner of the room where the men stood and introduced themselves. Étienne was the handsome Frenchman, the other man, Michel, a Canadian. Both were businessmen, Étienne explained, and friends for many years.

Angie explained that she was retired, traveling with her best friend from childhood, who had visited Paris many times.The men looked with interest at Marina and she realized she'd appear very rude if she didn't speak.

"Yes, I taught French and Art History for many years in a private school in New York. I love the French language. I'd enjoy speaking French with you, but let's speak English for Angie's sake, please."

"Of course. Michel is also fluent in both languages."

Étienne asked her where they'd visited and Marina told him of their forays into the Musée d'Orsay, the Rodin, the Picasso. She found herself slipping into French, and Étienne followed.

Angie turned her attention to Michel, asking him where in Canada he was from. A pleasant conversation ensued between them. Michel told her his wife had died a year ago and that he had two daughters and a baby grandson. Soon they were pulling out their phones, sharing family pictures, while Étienne and Marina continued to speak quietly in French.

Somehow, another round of drinks arrived and Angie looked worriedly at Marina, afraid she'd protest, but she only thanked Étienne and took a sip.

Halfway through the second cocktail Angie's conversation with Michel ran out of steam. Yet the stream of French conversation between Marina and Étienne flowed with an ease that impressed and, at the same time, irked Angie. She spoke to Michel.

"Didn't she say 'let's speak English for Angie's sake' just a few minutes ago? I do know basic French, but I can't follow them at all."

"Yes, they seem to have found their own rhythm. Perhaps we should leave them for a bit. I could show you other parts of the hotel. There's a lot to see."

"Oh, no, I don't think so."

"I'll bring you back to this spot in thirty minutes, I promise. You've nothing to fear from me." He reached over and spoke softly to his friend. "We'll return at ten o'clock, *d'accord?*"

"*Bien*," his friend said with a nod.

Marina stayed silent. Angie glared at her. What was wrong with her? For someone who'd just insisted on only one drink, promising to only be civil, she was behaving as if this Étienne was the only person in the world. Of course lovely Marina, tall and slender, would land the sexy Frenchman, while she, a short woman who might even be called "stocky"—after all, she'd given birth to four children—would end up with this skinny Canadian with pasty-looking skin.

Angie was able to let go of her resentment as Michel showed her the lobby and restaurant and translated the posted menu for her. The place was really amazing.

At precisely five minutes to ten Michel told her it was time to return to the bar and her anxiety rose up again. Would Marina be there? If not, would she be able to get back to their hotel? But when they reached the bar, Marina and Étienne were waiting for them just outside the entrance.

"How was your tour?" Marina asked.

"Lovely." Angie turned to Michel and put out her hand. "Thank you so much for showing me around the hotel. It was everything and more than I expected."

"And thank you for paying for the drinks," Marina said, reaching for Étienne's hand. "You are very generous."

"It was a pleasure," he said, kissing her hand. Marina smiled warmly. He also kissed Angie's hand and she couldn't help but be charmed by him. The evening hadn't played out as she'd expected, but it was fine. She'd had her adventure, she supposed.

The men escorted them outside and Michel hailed a taxi, paid the driver, and held the door for Marina and Angie. The women waved as the cab pulled away from the curb. Marina watched the lights of Paris as they sped toward their hotel, and Angie watched her friend. What on earth had happened in there? Was Marina going to spend the rest of her time here with Étienne?

They went quietly to their hotel room, Marina insisting that Angie use the bathroom first. While Marina got ready for bed, Angie got in bed and she took out a notebook and wrote about their day.

Hôtel Costes near the Place Vendôme. Très sensuelle. Met a Frenchman named Étienne and a Canadian named Michel. Interesting evening.

She continued to write as Marina got into bed and turned off her bedside lamp.

"Tired?" Angie asked.

"Yes. Maybe it was the two drinks or maybe the effort of holding up my end of a conversation in French, but I feel totally drained."

"Yet it looked to me like speaking with Étienne was the most natural thing in the world."

"That wasn't me. Not really," Marina said.

"What do you mean, it wasn't you?"

"It felt like someone took over my body and mind and the words just spilled out of me while I watched from above. A woman who looked just like me was conversing with a very attractive man who wasn't Jeff. It was very strange."

"What did you talk about? It was all too fast for me."

Marina turned onto her side and faced Angie. "I have no idea." She frowned. "I can't remember what we spoke about. Isn't that strange?" She was silent for a few minutes as Angie waited for more. "Now I remember. We spoke about grief. He just lost his elderly mother and his only sibling, his younger sister, both to cancer. I told him about being in Paris for the first time since Jeff died. We talked about reaching for our phones to call them every day. We talked about food we can no longer order, places we can't go because it reminds us of them, and the pain is so acute that we have to stop to catch our breath. I haven't really talked to anyone about this, not even you. I've kept it in, which can't be good. Speaking in another language just opened it up for me and, of course, being with someone who is in the same place as I am. Maybe that's why it didn't feel like me sitting at that table."

Angie thought about this before she spoke. "But it was you, Marina. It's a facet of you that maybe didn't exist before, but now it does. When Bill died, the kids called me every day, and one of them slept over every night for weeks, never leaving me alone. I don't know what they thought I'd do. I was grateful, but you can't grieve like that. When I sold the house and moved to the condo I locked myself in for a while and let myself feel it. The pain, I mean. And I got to the other side of it but at the same time I knew I'd carry it along with the memory of Bill for the rest of my life. And that's the way I live now. I look out the windows of taxis and pretend he's with me, seeing what I see." She reached across the space between the beds for Marina's hand. "But we'll survive, my friend," she said through her tears. "We'll live, we'll laugh, maybe we'll even love again, but we'll always remember."

They lay silently, watching the lights from the cars on the street play across the ceiling, their hands clasped together. Finally, they fell asleep and woke to a shining morning that they greeted with hope, carrying the memory of their husbands in their hearts.

Heidi Larsen

LATE SUMMER MEMORIES

Molly Chambers

Dedicated to H.B

She lives up on a hill.
Bales of newly mown hay line the road,
the last one before the dirt road begins.
Old railroad ties form the steps.
She sits in her favorite old chair,
surrounded by treasures from the past.
Her colonial ancestor with buttoned up vest, ponytail hairdo,
and short pants watches over her from his gold-framed portrait.
Curly hair fans out over the back of the chair.
Old pink and white crocheted blanket covers her,
a handmade gift from a friend in the past.
She smiles with a twinkle in her eye
letting me know she recognizes me this time.
Leaning forward she reaches out her hand for mine.
We talk about the people she loved,
so many of them are gone now.
She names off old friends,trapped like she is.
They call each other on the phone.
Hilltop homes, swollen limbs,
and miles of woods keep them apart.
She leans forward and points her finger in my direction,
"You remember, you remember," she says.
"I am sorry now that when I was younger,
I did not understand what it means
to have someone really listen to you."
97 years is not an easy place to be.

STORM

Marilynn Carter

snowflakes float and swirl

silence broken
by the howling of the wind

as far as the eye can see
whiteness prevails

frosted etchings
merge on the windows

no cars
no people

only whiteness

this is the heart of winter
blowing us her frosty kiss

A MOTHER'S LAMENT FOR HER LOST DAUGHTER

Molly Chambers

Your picture sits
next to my bedside,
your golden curls
tossed in the breeze,
your tawny brown skin
warmed by the sun.
Oh, how I long
to hold you again,
here in my arms.
How could death
have taken you
far from us
forever?
How can it be?
It was so fast;
we never believed.
It just cannot be.
I cannot hear
your sweet voice again
from the phone held to my ear.
There must be a way
we can snatch you one more time
from death's cold arms.
Oh, how I miss you so.
It cannot be
two long years you've been gone.

VIENTO SILVESTRE

Melissa Dorval

The words you spoke
about the past you didn't want
revealed aching sadness
behind your Borealis eyes

Each reality shared in whispers
wrapped around the fibers of my heart
like long and spindly fingers,
grasped and yanked

You did not deserve the takeaway
nor every broken thing
The hurt and the restarting,
such burdens on broad shoulders

Yet it's hard to scorn the makings
Of the grievous time-served path
When every wobbling step
provisioned you to me

From desert through the meadow
to hills and apple trees
Over pens and wooden tables
among bee sonnets and sweets

Through the months
and all our hopes,
past fears of unrequited
collided, you and I became us

And though we were strangers to kindness
we live like that no more
with every breath, each moment,
in you, I find, the wild winds of love

THE FINAL COUNTDOWN

Sue Moreines

Lying there, day after day, I wondered how other people did it. Survive, that is. I've heard the doctors say I was in a perpetual coma, breathing through a hole in my neck and kept alive by a gastric feeding tube. I wasn't able to see, communicate, move any part of my body or even feel if someone touched me. Although I could still hear, it wasn't always a good thing.

I was almost killed in a school bus accident when I was six, but instead, ended up like this. For 10 years, one long-term facility after another had watched over me, hoping to be the one that brought me back to life. Fat chance! My dad didn't handle things well and eventually divorced my mom. Although each visited when they could, all that did was give me a few moments of distraction from my nothing of a life.

I'll never forget the day the doctors held a meeting in my room to talk about my murder. Of course, they didn't call it that, but told my parents there was a teenager who needed a heart, and mine was a perfect match. They were asked to consider letting me go in order to save him, since my recovery was doubtful. The doctors explained in our state it was sometimes legal to discontinue all forms of nutrition, and my situation fit the bill. Then it was completely quiet, followed by shuffling and the squeaking of a door.

First of all, those doctors should have known better than to have that discussion in front of me. Did they forget some people can hear when they're in a coma? Idiots! Well, at least they let me in on the possible plan.

Anyhow, I'm sure you can imagine what it was like for me to lie there all night thinking about dying. It's not like I'd never thought about it before—I had, umpteen times. But I knew, deep down, I didn't want to die. I just wanted my life back.

Eventually, I made peace with dying. How could helping that boy live a long, happy, and normal life be a bad thing? I certainly had nothing important to lose but hoped when I slipped away it wouldn't hurt too much.

The next day, Dad came back and talked to me about the argument he had with Mom, but they apparently agreed to go through with the idea. He added that donating my heart to save the boy would ensure a part of me would live on.

Later that night, Dr. Shore visited to confirm what Dad had already told me.

She said, "Devin, this decision is one of the hardest things any parent should ever have to face. You've all gone through so much heartache, pain and loss over the years, and this isn't the way anyone wanted it to end. I know your mom, Jackie, was supposed to see you today, but she wasn't feeling well enough to come in. However, she assured me she will be here tomorrow."

Then, I was left to dwell in my silent world. Fortunately, I fell into a deep sleep, hoping to never wake up.

I learned later that Dad and Dr. Shore waited outside my room for Mom to arrive. When she never showed up, they went in and were shocked to see I was gone. Mom made it her mission to prolong my life by taking me out of the facility in the early hours of the morning, bringing me back to the protection of my own bedroom. I didn't understand how she was able to do that without getting into trouble, but found out she could do a lot of things because she was my health care agent.

Since I was home, Mom had to do all the scheduling so everything I needed was taken care of. Money wasn't an issue, because I received a lot from the accident. I had as many medical visits as required or anything else Mom wanted for me. There were appointments with physical and massage therapists, doctors, nurses, teachers and most often, visits with Pastor Shepherd. An aide was always with me, making sure I was moved every few hours, monitoring my breathing and fluid intake, and checking my body for any signs of irritation or bedsores.

Almost every day, for another five years, I wondered if Mom did the right thing, even though I really didn't want to die. Someone visiting me said most people don't stay in a coma for too long, and many become brain dead. Well, that didn't apply to me! I was amazingly patient, waiting for any kind of improvement. If only a miracle happened, as Pastor Shepherd repeatedly prayed about.

Dad still only stopped by every once in a while. He talked about sports, the weather, why he hated his job and other topics I couldn't care less about. I always wished he would tell me stories about what we did together before the accident or what he hoped I would be when I grew up. Only once did he say he loved me.

Mom wouldn't let any of my childhood friends come over, thinking it would be too hard on them. Hard on them? I would have loved hearing about their lives, finding out what it was like being a teenager and listening to things I missed over the past fifteen years...like everything!

One night, Mom told me she had something special planned for the next day. I couldn't imagine what that would be, since every day was pretty much the same. Maybe she arranged to have a therapy dog spend time with me. I always wished I had a dog of my own, but that wasn't likely to come true. Before I could think of anything else, Mom came into my room and announced,

"Just in case you forgot what today is, Devin, it's August seventeenth!! Happy twenty-first Birthday!"

Then she began to sing a very poor rendition of the "Happy Birthday" song before exclaiming,

"No one thought you'd reach this important milestone except for me, of course!"

Before Devin's mother could say another word, the house began to vibrate and then swayed violently from side to side. Devin's bed was hurled across the room and Jackie was thrown to the ground, knocking her unconscious. A tremendous seventy-five-year-old oak tree toppled onto the roof, creasing the ceiling of Devin's room. Swirling branches and debris smashed his windows, allowing leaves, acorns and sticks to flood inside. Soon, sirens began to scream, horns blared, and spotlights scanned the neighborhood. An earthquake had hit the area, causing significant destruction. Fires erupted, the power plant lost service, and the town was plunged into darkness and chaos.

Devin lay helpless, and a sharp piece of sheet metal had penetrated a portion of his skull. By the time emergency personnel made it to their house, Jackie began to regain consciousness. When she saw Devin, she wailed uncontrollably and needed to be escorted outside. All available medical staff were then able to focus their attention on Devin. His breathing was shallow, so they inserted a tracheal tube to ensure his lungs were getting enough oxygen. While monitoring vitals, the EMT's consulted with hospital physicians to determine how to proceed with his immediate care. Before he could be moved, they needed to be sure the metal in Devin's skull wouldn't shift, and the bleeding was controlled. Eventually, he was able to be airlifted to the nearest trauma center that had power and specialized services.

Two older EMT's remained on site after everyone else left. Leaning against a dresser, Robert said, "I'm in complete shock, Mike. I still get flashbacks about that accident. We did all we could to save everyone after the bus was broadsided by that speeding dump truck. I know there was nothing we could do to save the bus driver and those two young kids, but I still feel guilty."

"I know what you mean," said Mike. "I found Devin face down in the middle of the road with no signs of life. Since he wasn't breathing, I turned him onto his back and began CPR. He was only six years old, for God's sake, and there I was pounding on his chest, breathing down his throat and begging him to live. When the ambulance arrived, the paramedics took over until they could hook up the defibrillator and then quickly rushed him to the hospital."

"I heard he ended up in a coma, and assumed he later died," added Robert.

"How is it possible Devin lived for so long?" asked Mike.

Robert sighed, and said, "Absolutely no idea, Mike. And, who knows if he'll make it through this time. I can't imagine what it's been like for him over all these years. If it were me, I'd want to be dead, for sure."

Jackie was told Devin was on his way to a trauma unit about sixty miles away. She had no idea how and when she could get there and began to panic all over again. After a brief emotional breakdown, Jackie regained her composure and thought *I have no choice but to call Marshall. He should know what happened to Devin, and maybe he could find a way to get us to the hospital.*

"Jesus Jackie! Now this? It certainly doesn't sound like Devin's going to make it, but we have to go to the hospital. The roads are completely blocked within a mile of your house, so I'll pick you up at the gas station at the edge of town," responded Marshall.

Jackie did all she could not to call him an asshole for what he said about Devin, but didn't want to lose the ride. After filling a backpack with bottled water, snacks and a few necessary items, Jackie made it to the station well before Marshall did.

When Jackie got into the car, it wasn't hard for her to keep her mouth shut, since all she could do was think about Devin. However, Marshall eventually made another upsetting comment, which led to a shouting match.

"If I didn't need to be with Devin, I'd be out of this car in a second Marshall! I haven't asked you to help with Devin's care, let alone take a penny of your money. When are you going to let go of the idea that Devin should have been killed five years ago?" screamed Jackie.

Marshall swung the car over to the side of the road and screeched to a stop. Then, he leaned straight into Jackie's face and hollered, "Never! Never Jackie! I will never get over Devin having to endure being in a coma for 10 years! And your selfishness is the reason he was tortured for five more."

Jackie hunched over and sobbed while Marshall pulled back onto the highway and pushed the speed limit.

When they arrived at the hospital, they learned Devin was whisked into the operating room for emergency surgery to remove the metal that entered and fractured his skull. Jackie and Marshall paced the floor of the waiting room for more than two hours, avoiding eye contact and any conversation.

Finally, a doctor stood before them and said, "Good evening. My name is Dr. Williams, one of the many physicians involved in Devin's care. We removed the metal fragment, and it doesn't appear to have caused significant injury to his brain. However, the fracture will take time to heal, so being in a coma is an advantage for now. It's unclear how this head injury will affect his prior condition, and only time will tell. Devin is temporarily on a ventilator and appears to be resting comfortably."

"When can we see him, Doctor?" asked Jackie.

"Devin is in the recovery room, and when indicated will be transferred to the ICU. This may take a few hours, so you might want to consider going home or to a hotel for some rest," said Dr. Williams.

"I won't be leaving this waiting room until I'm able to see my son, Doctor.," said Jackie.

Marshall replied, "I'll be staying at a local motel. It's been a very long fifteen years, and I can only hope this recent incident won't make things worse for him, or the rest of us."

Jackie thanked Dr. Williams before he left, then bit her tongue and stared at Marshall as he walked out of the room. Then she sat down on a well-worn chair and dozed off and on until sunrise.

Marshall didn't return to the waiting room until mid-morning. About twenty minutes later, a nurse walked in and said Dr. Williams needed to speak with them.

Jackie grabbed her backpack and anxiously headed toward the office while Marshall ambled behind. The doctor sat at the head of a small conference table, surrounded by a number of empty chairs.

Dr. Williams didn't waste any time, starting to speak as soon as Jackie and Marshall appeared settled, "Devin needed more than six hours in the recovery room for a number of concerning reasons. His temperature, pulse rate, and blood pressure were not stabilizing, and even though he was on a ventilator, his oxygen level was not staying consistently high enough to keep him alive. To be painfully honest, it did appear the end was near. We did everything medically possible, and finally his oxygen saturation and vitals began to improve. However, thirty minutes later, Devin became physically agitated. That was an extremely unusual thing to happen, considering Devin has been in an extended coma, with no self-initiated movement."

Jackie's hands began to shake, and she blurted out, "Doctor, is it possible that's a sign Devin might be coming out of the coma?"

"It's possible, as agitation is sometimes seen with these types of patients, but I do not want to give you false hope," responded Dr. Williams.

"Hope is all I've had for fifteen years, Doctor, so, false or not, the chance of it happening fills my heart with joy," answered Jackie.

Marshall didn't say a word, but rolled his eyes and shook his head from side to side.

"The most recent update is this: Devin's vital signs and oxygen levels have remained stable for a significant amount of time, and there haven't been any further episodes of agitation. Devin was slowly weaned off the ventilator and is now breathing on his own," said Dr. Williams.

"Devin's room in the ICU is currently being prepped for him. It will take some time for everything to be set up to safely and effectively manage his medical and supervision needs. Once in the ICU, Devin will be very closely watched to ensure that the stability he attained in the recovery room continues. Without wanting to increase your anxiety, I need to reiterate, Devin is still in a very fragile and unpredictable state, based on what happened post-surgery. Please keep this in mind as you wait," warned Dr. Williams.

Jackie and Marshall returned to the waiting room, where Jackie picked up her phone and placed a call.

"Hello Pastor Shepherd, this is Jackie Baldwin, Devin's mom. Devin was injured during the earthquake, and Marshall and I are at the hospital. He suffered a skull fracture requiring surgery, and will be admitted to the ICU. If it's possible for you to join us, I know Marshall and I could benefit from your spiritual guidance, moral support, advice, and belief in the healing power of prayer."

"Are you out of your mind Jackie? What I just heard is the final countdown for Devin has begun. I'm not going through this again," shouted Marshall, before kicking over a chair and barging out of the room.

"I'm on my way Jackie. Until I get there, focus on your strength, determination, abilities, and love; that will help get you through this very difficult time," said Pastor Shepherd.

Jackie did all she could to stop her body from shaking and her thoughts from racing toward hopelessness. First, she paced the halls, then climbed up and down the steps in the stairwells to lessen her nervous energy. When she went back to the waiting room, Jackie sat down and closed her eyes. Within seconds, she began to think about holding Devin's hand as they walked to the bus stop on his first day of school. Through his tiny fingers she could feel his excitement about beginning first grade and remembered how hard she had to work to control her own anxiety about him leaving her. Jackie's thoughts were soon interrupted by Dr. Williams, who told her she could finally see Devin.

"Thank you so much, Doctor," began Jackie. "Marshall stormed out, and probably won't be back. I called Pastor Shepherd, who is on his way here. Will he be allowed to stay with me during the visit?"

"Absolutely," said the doctor, at the exact moment the Pastor appeared.

As soon as Jackie saw Devin lying in bed she said, "Something is not right with him. It's not because his head is bandaged, or his color is a bit off, or even that he's connected to more equipment than in the past."

Jackie reached over and pulled down the sheet covering

Devin's body. She stared at him from head to toe and said, "Is it my imagination, or is Devin's chin pulled down a bit closer to his chest? His head always leaned as far back as it could go. And, look at his hands. They usually lay flat down and limp against the mattress. Now, his palms are facing up and his fingers seem to be slightly raised."

Dr. Williams, the nurses, and Pastor Shepherd listened intently, and paid very close attention to Jackie's observations. Moments later, Devin had a seizure. Every part of his body twitched and moved, and his eyes opened and closed.

"Oh my God! What's going on?" screamed Jackie.

Dr. Williams and multiple nurses surrounded Devin's bed. One nurse placed her hand on his body to help keep him calm, others turned Devin onto his side. Pastor Shepherd prayed and the monitors made loud beeping sounds. Dr. Williams injected lorazepam into the intravenous line, and within moments Devin lay still.

"I wish I could tell you exactly what just happened and why, but I can't," said the doctor. "The metal that penetrated Devin's skull barely entered his brain, and the fracture was linear. That means there was a break in the skull, but the bone did not move. I will be ordering a number of scans and tests to better determine what might be going on."

The visit needed to be terminated, so Jackie and the pastor went back to the waiting room where Jackie cried and the pastor did his best to help keep her spirit strong.

Every thirty minutes a doctor or nurse would come to the waiting room to keep Jackie and the pastor informed about the ups and downs Devin was experiencing. He had another seizure, his blood oxygen level fluctuated wildly, and episodes of occasional agitation returned. It took many hours before Devin's vital signs and physical condition stabilized.

Eventually, Jackie and Pastor Shepherd were allowed to return to Devin's room. Jackie looked at Devin with tears in her eyes, but spoke in a confident and cheerful voice. She reached over, held his hand and said, "Remember what I told you the other day, Devin? It was your twenty-first birthday, and I had something special planned for you. I'm so sorry the earthquake got in the way of that."

Jackie opened her backpack, took out an envelope, a birthday sign, and brightly colored paper balloons, before saying, "Devin, it's never too late to celebrate, so I made sure to bring the party here."

Pastor Shepherd hung up the birthday sign, the nurses put the balloons around Devin's bed, and, as Jackie began to open the card, some of Devin's monitors began to beep. Two nurses ran to his side and took his vitals manually, since the devices were not recording any abnormalities.

Jackie never looked away from Devin, taking in every inch of him. Moments later, she noticed a single tear roll down his cheek and his eyelids began to flutter. Jackie held his hand again, and to everyone's amazement, Devin slowly opened both eyes. He looked directly at his mother and mouthed the words, "I love you, Mom."

Pastor Shepherd smiled and said, "Yes, miracles do happen!"

WINDSWEPT WAY

Phyllis A. Cochran

Headed down life's pathway,
seeking distant shores,
guided by worldly pleasures,
caught up in family chores.

Keepsakes stored in the attic,
heaped with dust and age.
In awe I watched my children,
struggling through each stage.

I lent strength and wisdom,
for them to always clutch.
Our home, a helmet of love,
that trials dare not touch.

Dreams like starlit nights,
burst forth on cloudy days,
till sorrow's silent curse,
cradled death's dark maze.

Our child gone too soon,
caused brokenness and tears.
Nightmares of her absence,
awakened all my fears.

I yearned to understand,
Heaven, God's seeming bliss.
His light unmarked by doubting,
opened blind eyes to this.

My detour clad with wings,
wove a pathway new,
to walk in the master's steps,
seeking a higher view.

God's crossroad paved with freedom,
tore the bars away,
placed truth within my heart;
changed my windswept way.

CONSUMMATION OF EARTH AND WIND

Kathy Bennett

Despondency assimilates to the doldrums. The world of meteorology, however, knows the term as an intertropical convergence zone where there is little wind and where ships cannot sail.

Legend has it that The Doldrums are where the wind is born…

Passion sleeps between her meridian poles.
The last trace of her beatitude so fair and chaste
She tiptoed out like a lover in the night,
His whispered words a zephyr in her ear.

Doldrum rumblings stir within,
Somewhere between her northernmost
And her nethermost environs.
Inklings and tinklings murmur there.

Love and life itself
Wrestle within her equatorial regions —
Where the wind is born —
Desire, quickened and carnal,

Oscillates among all her senses,
Tempestuously swirling
The savage seas;
An expression of her rain dance.

The breath of the Sylph,
Like molten lava caressing her,
Rustles her palmetto lushness.
And in the cyclone of all her wicked whirling,
Her *Passionwind* effuses into the soul of another.

SOARING ON THE WILD WINDS OF MEMORY

Karen Traub

A zephyr is a gentle breeze that swirls and caresses, sometimes coming up from nowhere. If you listen close enough, ghosts of the past may whisper secrets for you alone to hear.

"Don't cry mama," I wanted to say, but I didn't even have the strength to move my lips. I could picture my beautiful Mama taking a moment to "compose" herself as she called it. She would dab her eyes with her handkerchief, smooth her dress, and breathe deeply before coming over to my bed where she spent most days and nights, holding my hand, stroking my hair, feeding me soup if I could eat or trying to tempt me with the applesauce sprinkled with cinnamon that she knew I loved.

If I could, I would give her courage like she gave me the time my big brother Charlie broke the head off my baby doll. "Buck up dear one," she'd said, in a voice more encouraging than scolding. "You are a loved child in a fine home, there are much worse things that can happen." I guess this was one of them. You see, it was March 4, 1892, I was six years old and in three weeks, I would be dead.

My sweet mama, called Carrie by her friends and "Mrs. Hamilton" by the housekeeper hired to take her place after she married my father, pulled her chair closer to my bed, reached her loving hand to feel my forehead for fever, and spoke softly as she always did.

"I have a letter for you, pet," she said. "It's from our Lura. Charlie picked it up from Berry farm on his way home from Prescott." I tried to open my eyes, but all I could do was flutter my eyelids. I wanted her to know I was listening. "She says she is sorry Dearie cannot visit today, as the wind still blows and she has the headache too." I wasn't sure if I was dreaming or awake, it made so little difference these days, but her voice was comforting. "She sends a photograph of Bessie to Charlie." Mama paused and said to me, "Oh, how I wish you could open your eyes and see it." I imagined Bessie Berry with her long dark hair in ringlets, her serious eyes and her pale, thin face. She was sweet on Charlie but he was more interested in throwing rocks in the river and fishing, than in girls like Lura's younger sister Bessie. "She wishes she had a picture of you…and so do I," Mama told me and then made a sound like clearing her throat with a gulp and a sniffle.

Days and nights went by I guess, but I wasn't really aware of time. Whenever I woke, someone was beside me, usually Mama. Once I heard Doctor Wright's voice. He had always been kind, since the first time I heard him say the awful words "Diabetes Mellitus." Today his voice seemed far away. "So sorry… keep her comfortable...make arrangements."

Mama's sad face was the last I saw as I floated toward the light. And then I was riding on the wind. Flying above, soaring like a bird. I was free. I watched while my body, inside a pine box was slowly lowered into the ground. Mama, eyes red and cheeks wet, sobbed like the dam had broken and all the tears in the world were spilling out. How I wish she could see me. "I'm up here Mama! I'm happy and free!" Mary and Lura stood on each side of Mama, holding her up, while they also wept. My brother Charlie, my father, and my grandfather, who Mama called "Mr. Hamilton" to his face, and "the old man," when he wasn't around, stood together silently in their fine suits looking like the gentlemen they were.

After it was over, Mama tucked the note from Lura Berry

into my sewing box which held the squares of fabric for the quilt I would never make, and the needle case and silver thimble that were among my most treasured possessions. Mama kept that box for the rest of her life, through the troubles with Charlie and his early death, and when she was old and had to move from our home, she gave it to Mary who kept it at the library and later the town vault. And there it would stay for a hundred years—until someone opened it who cared enough to tell my story.

Author's note: It was a regular Tuesday morning in mid-September when I found myself in Old Town Hall, sitting at the table whose top was pitted with a hundred years of pens signing birth, marriage and death certificates, annual reports, and tax records. As a library trustee, I was taking inventory of items belonging to, but not stored at the MN Spear Memorial library in Shutesbury, Mass. "Why," I wondered, "was there a sewing box that belonged to the library?" I opened the box and looked through its contents and, unknown to me at the time, the spirit of the little girl issued forth like a genie from a bottle and possessed me. I needed to learn the story of little Lucy Hamilton. I needed to know who Lura Berry was, whether Lucy got well, and what happened with Bessie and Charlie. Over the next several years I learned as much of their stories as I could through town records and census data. My imagination filled in the rest.

FLIRTING WITH LIGHT AND SHADE

William Doreski

Between Petersham and Barre
the road sloughs through windy forest
glum with flies and gargling streams.
No fishermen, though. Sunday traffic
rushes home, breasting the gale.

I park in a rutted turnout
peppered with beer cans and step
a few feet into the pines and stretch
and gaze into flickering boughs.
I can read your face there, spirit

of gloomy childhood landscapes.
You'd laugh to learn I've imposed
your memories of Siberia
on this patch of Massachusetts woods.
But if you saw the sunlight tatter

in the crowns of these slim red pines
you'd agree to haunt this spot
forever, mainly to rebuke me.
At my feet a narrow brook snores
down the slope, ducks under the road

to reach the Swift River and then
empty into Quabbin Reservoir.
When I picture you entwined
with an entire continent,
as you so often seem to be,

I'm sure you've energy enough
to inflame so modest a spot

in my private atlas. And here
you are, flirting with light and shade.
And here I am, stretching halfway

through a long drive. You're the spirit
and I'm the flesh, a distinction
we acknowledge even face to face,
running water and windy treetops
implicit in our greetings.

ILL WINDS

MY BEATING HEART

Justine Johnston Hemmestad

The job I tended to was menial and obscure, but I needed the money, and my wife allowed me to play devil's advocate in my own life. I was as good of a detective as any I had created in Dupin – nay, I was better, for Dupin was modeled on *me*. But expenses in a world of fine dining and theater, horses and carriage rides, gambling and fine clothes, was a constant drudge upon my soul; for the time I was forced to fret over money when I could have been writing imprisoned me into a brick wall. I had to be resourceful and write when no one knew I was writing, whether in the darkened buggy or in the darkened house. I had to move forward despite the resistance of debt collectors, plaguing me with their demands. The stories I conjured in my mind in the long nights spent staying with the old man across town were equal to a witches' brew, and the setting in which I found myself fostered my imagination…despite the occasional sound of horses in the road or the raven that so often tormented me from the windowsill. My nature was to thrash through darkness until I found a mystery, and the old man rarely had me light a candle in his house.

I braced my jaw and squared my shoulders as I stepped out of the buggy before the old man's dark house, which possessed withered arms in place of trees that whipped in the wind, and imposing sneers in place of windows and a door. There were secrets that slithered from the house and nestled into the corners of my brain, though I had yet to confront them so that I may discover what their provocations were. My goal, well beyond the old man, was to understand myself, for if there was ever a time to learn the impetus of my inspiration, the old man for whom I worked, and the house he lived in, presented it. Unlike Oedipus, who stood before his father and slew him without awareness of whom he had killed, I stood before the old man in full awareness of my murderous intention; I stood at the bottom of his steps, the wind rattling the windows, the raven tapping at the glass, and wrung my hands. I took a deep, concentrated breath, and walked toward the door, ruminating on how the old man probed into my life, and especially worrisome, he knew about my wife. He was only mildly familiar to me, I knew not from where.

The work had almost been worth it though, for my duties to the old man afforded me free time to compose poems, many of which breathed new life into my literature. The critics and rivals may not know it, but I yielded credit to their careers. I gave them something to emulate. My writing was as ominous as my life, but that, I could not help, for the words arose from my soul. No other method was available to me in which I could banish the daemons that haunted me. In no other way could I reckon with what happened to Jane. That old man plagued me with interruptions and demands. Every time my mind was on track, the old man managed to scatter my most vital thoughts.

I contemplated murdering him in his sleep, for I could think of no other way to escape his judgment of me. I hoped that writing would serve as the detective of my own past, or even of his. There had to be a key that unlocked the truth of the past, and my duty was to watch for the clues. I tilted my chin back, gained all my courage, and stepped through the entryway with a natural scuff of my shoe. The howling wind outside was all I could hear when I shut the door behind me, for the window was unable to withstand the drafts, and the curtains themselves shifted.

The old man lurked around me during the days even though he could not rise from his bed, and always stared at me with evil eyes as I walked through. I could not escape him, nor could I escape his examination of me. During the nights, I secretly peered into his room, concentrating on the slowly melting candles of the candelabra on the table beside his bed, for the sinking wax somehow manipulated time, and the flames that flickered and danced reflected onto the single, uncovered window. The window and the twisted, dull metal of the candelabra were adjoined by haunting cobwebs that seemed to spin an alternate world into the darkness outside. My heart seized when the old man called me to his bed, as he often did when night overcame day. I tried to look into his eye and search for his secrets. I tried to place him in my memory.

I could smell his ancient flesh the same as I could smell the floorboards rotting beneath my shoes, or the decaying corpses in the graveyard behind the house. I could feel headstones on my fingers in the guise of feet and legs. No water was wet enough to wash away the smell of decaying flesh. Though my young wife had been to the house before, the old man never seemed to take notice. He simply stared at me with his evil eye, as though he had the power to hide me away forever, in service of his own distasteful ends.

"Come closer, and tell me what you remember of Jane," the old man grumbled. *Why must he throw a wrench into my heart?* I wondered. To render him silent, I had visions of torturing him and smothering the life out of him, a welcomed thought amidst his devilish insanity. Oh, I could presume what he was thinking, and, in fact, I knew his state of mind all too well. I just needed to find out how much he *really* knew.

I casually crossed the threshold of his room. "Sir," I answered. "Do you need me?"

"Come here, boy, and let me look at you."

"Sir, I beg your pardon." I acknowledged, as I drew further into his room. Secretly, I harbored the deepest, darkest thought that tonight would be the very night I might snuff the life out of him. The pillows lay ready beside his head. All I needed to do was snatch one and hold it steadily over his face. No one would ever know, not even the detectives who would surely come by later to investigate. Most of all, I could never allow the old man to so much as perceive my intention as I drew nearer to his bedside.

"Boy," he said to me, "there is something I have not told you, something I must tell you now."

My murderous inclinations were unwillingly stalled. I took a shallow breath and said, "I am certain that whatever needs to be said can be said in the morning."

"This cannot wait," he wheezed. "You need to admit the truth to yourself."

The old man appeared more frail than he had at any other time—though his single opened eye was luminous and all-seeing. His stare made me cringe. I took a step closer to the bed. "What is it?" I questioned through clenched teeth.

"I know what is troubling you tonight," he said, "and I need to tell you something before you leave here again." I bit my bottom lip as he continued to investigate me. "Have you wondered why I employed you, even though you were a stranger to me? And why I brought you into my house, even though you have your own family?"

I shook my head. "My reason has been a secret to you, but now I will tell you." The old man inhaled deeply, his eye unwavering, his jaw shrinking with his closed mouth. The thought that I should seize the moment and push the pillow down onto his face darted through my mind. But he interrupted my thought by speaking again. "I knew Jane. She was a delicate woman. She showed me the same poetry she showed you."

I could feel the tightness of my brow as I narrowed my eyes. "Why are you telling me this?" I demanded.

"I know your secret; I know you loved Jane. She knew you loved her, but she knew she could never return your love, because you were too young. She died of a broken heart, because she loved you, and you were unproven, but *you* did not kill her like you thought," he coughed. "She died because she asked me to help her die. It was the only way she could be completely free of you."

I took a step back from the bed. "Stop these lies, old man," I seethed. "Jane is my wife! We are happy." There was no question in my mind that I would be able to carry out my murderous intentions now, for the musty air I sharply inhaled was primed to welcome death.

"It is not a lie, I helped her die," he said to me, his one eye unblinking. "I gave her the laudanum to do it; she could not live with her guilt. You *have to* admit that. She gave you the poetry books to stir a love in you for the written word, not to stir love in you for her. Listening to you read the poems stirred love in her for *you*." The old man sighed, clutching the blanket up to his chest with both hands. "Jane could have been a poet herself, and she was so very beautiful. You were nothing but a boy when she died, and her husband was making her life a living hell. I am certain she would have told you the truth about loving you if she lived. She knew she would *have* too, and that is why she wanted to die."

I squeezed my eyes shut and shook my head. "No! Stop this! I married her. We are in the midst of a full life."

"Face the truth, Edgar. You did not marry her, because *she killed herself*. She is dead — you need to admit it so you can live your life and stop living in the past. Remember, boy, remember the truth. It is time you accept that."

I stopped and met the old man's eye, hoping that he would die on his own. I knew, deep in my mind, that he was a murderer.

Flashes of memory intruded my thoughts…a graveyard that was not in the backyard of the house in which I stood, a sinking feeling in the pit of my stomach. I had to ask him, with all the desperation I felt, "Did she ask you for the laudanum, or did you give it to her without her knowledge?"

"You were only a boy, infatuated with your friend's mother!"

"Stop saying that I was a boy! I was far from a boy —" I seethed, "I was on the verge of manhood."

"I carried out her wishes."

"No," I said loudly, my hands pressed to the sides of my head as though I could squeeze the wicked old man's lies out. "She was in my dreams before I met her; indeed, she was fused into my soul. We were bound by poetry, until *you took her from me.* I live, carrying the weight of her death around my neck. I believed it was my fault because I loved her, when all along it was *you* who caused her death. A few more years and we would have married," I shook my head frantically. "I wanted to believe we had! What made you think you could cast judgment over us?"

"You brought her misery on. Even if you were on the verge of manhood…you were too young and too close," the old man weakly insisted. I knew that was all I could take; the old man was a murderer. A powerful gust of wind must have knocked limbs from the tree outside, for the thuds on the house stopped my heart for an instant. But I narrowed my eyes; I had wanted to wait until he fell asleep to kill him, but I snatched up the pillow from behind his head, and held it in both hands above his face. I slammed it down with great force. The back of his head hit the headboard with a thud. The old man's muffled cries were meek and to no avail. He first held his arms out as though to grip *my* arms, but my mind was made up. I ignored his muffled cries. I was not going to stop. This old man had taken the life of my greatest love, and I needed to take *his* life.

When his lifeless hands finally fell from my forearms, I knew it was over. I took a single step back from the bed, but the claws of interest held me within the room; the old man made no move, not even a twitch. I tossed the pillow onto the foot of the bed. Then I turned and ran out of the room and down the stairs. My flight took me to the common room by the hutch where the silverware was stored, where I stopped to catch my breath and think about the old man's confession. I gazed into the streaked mirror affixed to the back of the cabinet, and stared as though my reflection could give me the answers I so vehemently sought. Each time I saw my eyes blink, I heard the beating of my own heart. I knew I had to police *my own mind.* I slammed my fist onto the hutch, jolting a rusted spoon off the edge to clank upon the floor; a thought shot through my mind about the man's younger, drug-induced days. Next to where the rusted spoon rested, an opened book's pages suddenly fanned out as though the air itself had fingers.

I squinted and bent down toward the book. I recognized it, for it was one of Jane's poetry books. I wondered why it was on the floor in the old man's abode. My heart leapt out from its pages, as though my life was bound to her through the poetry that the old man had stolen. My heart pounded louder and louder, until I could stand it no more. I clutched the book and threw it across the room toward the fire in the hearth. Sparks tossed into the air and a thicker smoke arose.

I could not imagine her with the old man, even in his youth. I knew he was but a surreal part of the atmosphere in which I survived. I could not help but wonder, could she have loved him as I had loved her? I longed for a stone-cold heart, a heart that felt nothing, a heart that merely lived in the world because it was meant to…and yet it was a heart that someone else could cleanse with love. I gazed at my reflection in the mirror again. The edges were methodically blurred and seemed to slowly shift outward. My reflection had come to life, even while I continued to glare at myself with an internal rage. I slammed both fists down upon the hutch, jolting the glass shooters beside a decanter of alcohol.

"Boy!" I heard sharply through the house. The call was deafening, even more so than the shrieking wind outside. I stared into the mirror. I had gone insane. "Boy!"

My eyes opened wide in horror. I peered toward the stairs. No, I could not allow myself to believe that the old man was still alive; I would not go up. I squeezed my brow, like I had squeezed the life from him. "Shut up old man, you are dead," I said to myself. "I killed you like you killed Jane."

"Boy, come up here! I am not done talking to you."

I shook my head but stepped slowly toward the stairs. I knew rationally that if he was not dead, I had to finish the job, for Jane's sake. I took one precise step up at a time, trying to avoid the creak in the middle. My breathing was shallow, scarcely heard by even myself. "Listen, old man," I said under my breath, "you are meant to die; you will call me 'boy' no more." I softly stepped toward the old man's room and pushed on the door, which opened with a loud groan. The old man, who had been sprawled over the bed in death, suddenly sat up. I could not believe my eyes; I blinked heavily.

"Listen, boy," he said. His eye was still listless, but it was not consuming my attention as much as it had only moments before. I was stunned more than I had been upon learning of Jane's death. The pounding of my heart could not be ignored, for it sent the whole house into a haunting rhythm.

"You are dead," I said blankly. "I felt you stop breathing. I saw you go limp."

The old man ignored me. "I have not thanked you, boy," he uttered breathlessly.

"Stop calling me 'boy!' You should not thank me. I killed you. Lay down on your deathbed."

"You sent me to be with Jane, boy. I told her I would have her in death, and now I do."

Aghast, I shook my head. "You cannot mean that."

"I do mean it. No one else knows that I sent her on before myself, no one but you."

"I murdered you tonight. The deed is done."

"You did what I wanted you to do. You sent me to Jane," he said, his countenance fallen as though lifelessness were returning to him.

"I sent you to hell."

"You sent yourself to hell," he wheezed. I immediately turned away from the old man, for he was dead, and I needed to not waste my time conversing with a ghost.

I rushed back down the stairs, over the floorboards, and stood on the worn wooden floor before the hutch. I stared into my distorted reflection in the mirror again, when the old man called, "Boy!" I wondered how to silence the murderer, if being murdered was not enough. I had uncovered the truth, I had gotten him to admit his misdeed, and yet he taunted me even in death. I would simply ignore him. I sat down in the chair beside the hearth, otherwise pleased with my deduction.

"Lift up those loose floorboards, there, at your feet," the old man suddenly appeared beside me in the shadows and spoke. I was stunned; my jaw hung low. I had never seen him standing on his own recognizance before. "Go ahead, move the rug over," he breathed.

I leaned down and flopped the rug over upon itself, then clicked one of the floorboards with the heel of my shoe. I tried to wedge my fingertips into the crevice befitting the next. When one finger of one hand found the crack, I slowly lifted it up, unsure of what I would find. In the same way I lifted another floorboard, then a third. I could not trust this man, this murderer of beautiful women, but I had to continue. I set the loose board to the side and slid onto one knee, peering into the void. "I see only darkness," I said.

"There is more than darkness. Look closer."

I bent closer to the void, lowering one hand cautiously, but deliberately, within. My heart was beating so loudly that my chest ached; the sound was pounding in my ears so loudly that I wondered if the local police could hear it. I wanted to tear my heart out of my breast and leave it beneath the floorboards where my hand now searched; my fingers grasped and fumbled at the burlap sack I now touched. "You have sacks down here," I uttered. "I know not how many."

"You thought the only graveyard was behind the house," he wheezed. "I tell you there is another one beneath the floorboards of this house." He stepped back from me, hunched over though raising his arms out. I could not breathe. "This is the house," he said, "that I bought for her. This was where we would live. She hated her husband, and I would have rescued her; but she loved *you.* I was pushed to the wayside for a *boy* with nothing to his name but poetry."

"If you really knew her, you would have known that poetry was her *greatest* wealth." I took a deep breath and looked up. Then, I peeked over my shoulder and decided to wiggle another of the floorboards up, then another. The musty odor was stronger than I had ever imagined; animals must have gotten themselves caught below and rotted away. My nose curled and I coughed, and yet I continued to yank up the floorboards.

"That is enough," the old man said. "You do not need to open the hole up any more to know what I have buried in there. You understand, I did bring her back with me, to this house, meant for her to live out the rest of her days with me."

"She is buried in the town cemetery with her family," I

countered, almost in a trance. I dreaded what he would tell me next.

"No, she is not. I took her from that place — she did not want to be there. She wanted to escape her husband, not spend an eternity with him." The old man stared down to the opened floorboards and said, "I took her out of there in the dead of night and brought her here, to live with me, forever."

"You are mad!" I screamed as I shot to my feet.

"That I may be, but now I am also dead."

"And you chose to do *this*?"

"I have my revenge against you, boy. You stole Jane's heart and she died for it, so I have crushed your make-believe life."

"No!" I yelled and reached out for him to effortlessly fling him into the hole beneath the floorboards I had removed. I could not see an end to what lay beneath, only darkness, and the old man did not scream — for he was already dead. Indeed, there was not the resistance of flesh and bone when I pushed him in, but he followed where my mind willed him. Truly, he lay dead in the bed upstairs; I had opened Jane's grave, and I laid her back in it. I had uncovered the old man's secret: the house was Jane's tomb.

I backed away from the loosened floorboards in a stupor and glanced into the mirror at the hutch. My expression was the same. My eyes were encircled by darkness, deep wrinkles lined my forehead, with lighter ones crossing my eyes and mouth. I stared, burning the glass with my gaze. I tried to see something, anything at all, that reminded me of my love, for I strove to be a writer for *her*. Now my inspiration was gone. Then, I saw a turn of my brow, a lift in the right corner of my lips, and my low-set ears that allowed me to hear the faintest deception. I had learned the truth for *her*, and I would never let it rest. Her truth would break free through the stories I wrote, *I would free her with my pen*. The house would no longer be her tomb.

FALLING FOR IT

Chele Pedersen Smith

I fell off the cliff countless times,
but only in my mind.
From the heightened ledge,
I jumped, hurled,
imagining the earth's floor closing in
to meet me.

But would it stop the pain, the anguish, or the angry ball of stress
festering within?

Tumbling through mental molecules,
I saw the menaces cut in front of me.
Life's challenges gained speed and zipped ahead.
"Good!" I laughed. "Let them crash and burn."

But below, I saw them thriving, multiplying, and morphing
into thorns and hungry piranhas waiting for my touch-down.
The demons were on guard to perforate and chomp.

They'd chew me up,
leaving gristly matter and parts of me too feeble to fight back.
How good does easy prey taste, anyway?

Just as I neared the frenzy, a gust of suggestions swooped in,
cradling me in a billowing cape.
In an updraft, I was propelled and placed back on the cliff.
I thanked the ideas kindly, and climbed down the hill.
Why let problems win?
I took a deep breath and exhaled.
Picking up my spear, I was ready to kick ass.
With creativity and logic, I'd conquer those nuisances one by one.
As I opened the dilemma door, what do you know?
Some had already left.

HERMIT IN THE WOODS

Lorri Ventura

Despite the rumor that she ate children
I looked for her
As I rode my horse along the overgrown, old lumberjack trail.
Once I saw her drifting toward me among the towering oaks.
At first I thought she was a rag-clad ghost,
Her skin translucent,
Waist-length hair colorless
And adorned with brown leaves.
Nostrils flared,
My palomino shied away from her fusty odor.
As if possessed,
I slowly reached into my saddle bag.
Hands trembling,
I held out the carrot packed
As a treat for my mount.
The woman crept toward me.
Then, fast as a beam of light,
She grabbed with a vine-like hand,
And devoured the root tuber.
Subtly tugging on the bridle's reins,
I backed up,
Worried that the specter was eyeing me
As her lunch entree.
But then she dropped to her knees,
Head bowed and hands clasped as if in prayer,
Giving me both leave and benediction.
I never told my parents,
Knowing that they'd forbid me ever again to ride in the forest.
But whenever I rode down that path
I packed an extra sandwich or snack
In case the woman re-appeared.
Never again did she grace me with her presence
No matter how hard I searched.

PREVAILING WESTERLIES

Tricia Knoll

When you live by the Pacific Ocean,
the wind brings a hefty breath.
New. Fresh. Then debris from Fukushima
washes up, pieces of wall board and
boat hulls from currents pushed in sea circles
and air aloft. No more romance of glass
Japanese fishing floats. You reckon
it took months to bring what's broken over

and the trade winds sigh and chuff
raw and salty. If it crosses
the ocean, it's cleansed, you think.
Romancing the wind.

Today's forecast said Vermont got soot
from the wildfires on the Pacific coast
in Canada. Not to worry to inhale
this high-altitude bit of dimming
sky down, not lung cancer stuff?

The Northeast gets second-hand.
New Orleans claims the river
water has been through
twelve kidneys before
it gets to the delta,
let's-not-think-about-it-reuse.

I'LL CALL TOMORROW

Mark Schafron

Mr. Richard lived alone in a town of shaded streets in a country of four seasons. Medium-tall with pale blue-gray eyes and a thick head of white hair, he used an aluminum cane, and kept black-framed reading glasses hooked in his shirt front. He had been widowed for so long that when he thought of her, he had to strain to hear her voice. As for her face—the healthy, glowing, smiling face from the time before her sickness—he saw it as if through a diaphanous veil. Most of his other waking memories had lost color, dimension, and motion as well, rendering themselves as faded gray tintypes.

Mr. Richard spent most nice afternoons in his front yard, sitting in a lawn chair shaded by an old crabapple tree. Next to his chair he kept a small cooler stocked with bottled water and a pint of liquor. He would sit, hearing indistinct threads of conversation from passersby, and watch the morphing clouds and the birds gliding on the winds aloft. Sometimes he held harsh, muttered hindsight conversations with people who, if still living, had long ago forgotten about him.

Mr. Richard hugged slights close to his chest, while ennui wrapped around him like a leaden cloak.

When the yard filled with shadows, he would go inside and heat what he found in the freezer, then settle into his recliner and reflexively flick the television remote. Sometimes, once it was dark, he would stand in a window looking toward a distant causeway, and watch the lines of marching car lights, soft and sulfurous in the fog. When the gray tintypes of memory began to gather, Mr. Richard went to sleep early, helped along by his pint of liquor.

This afternoon was different. He was standing in the shadows of his stifling attic, looking out the open window, waiting for the young man with the multicolored hair. The varying hues of the fellow's hair fascinated Mr. Richard. His late wife had colored her honey brown hair when it grew back shock white after the first bout with chemo. She paid a pretty penny for a blend of professionally applied pigments that mimicked her natural color. To Mr. Richard, the young man looked as if he'd smeared his hair with finger paint.

But the issue wasn't his hair, it was his dog. An ordinary, paroled-from-the-shelter mutt.

The dog had chronographic regularity, because it defecated in Mr. Richard's front yard near the sidewalk—at the exact same time—almost daily. Mr. Richard would watch from his lawn chair and loudly clear his throat as the young man tried to walk off and leave it. The young man would sullenly shuffle back to the mess and clean it up with a plastic bag, then walk off glaring over his shoulder.

It was the same routine almost every day, for many days, until one afternoon when Mr. Richard cleared his throat, the young man simply raised his middle finger without looking and kept walking.

Now, Mr. Richard watched as they rounded the corner and came down the street. As soon as the dog squatted, Mr. Richard drew back on a handmade, Huck Finn slingshot, and nailed the dog on the haunch with a tiny pebble. The dog jumped and yanked his owner down the street, while the young man looked all around.

Back in his chair in the shade, Mr. Richard was not surprised when the young man and his dog returned with a beat cop. The day was warm and the cop was sweating in his body armor.

"This guy says you shot his dog," the cop said.

"What? I don't know this kid and I don't own any firearms."

"It was a slingshot," the young man said. "I heard it snap."

Mr. Richard leaned forward in his lawn chair. He held up his hands and affected an arthritic curl to his fingers.

"I can barely hold a pencil, let alone a slingshot. And I like dogs."

"Come on," the cop said sharply to the young man. "Your dog probably got stung by a bee."

As they walked up the street, the young man looked over his shoulder. Mr. Richard smiled and raised his middle finger.

Mr. Richard would dream almost every night. In some he walked in a fugue, where sights and sounds came and went through a heavy twilight mist. Others were vivid and painted in bright otherworldly colors—memories, really, that he would not allow himself to reflect upon while awake. This night he dreamed of the horses of his boyhood. Their rich herbivore scent. The satisfaction of caring for them—currying and brushing them one after another as they stood cross-tied in the barn. The way their eyes half closed and their heads drooped as he worked. His pride in having their trust. He never ran them too hard during exercise laps or was rough on their mouths with the bit like the other stable boys could be. Sometimes, he would just lean on the fence and watch them clustered in the paddock, their tails swishing. One by one they would walk over to him, snorting and blowing. He'd dig in the pocket of his tattered barn coat and feed each one a fresh carrot. To their distant owners they were livestock or investments—to him they were beloved pets. When they were sold off, he hid in the hayloft and cried as he listened to the metallic stomp of their being led into trailers.

When he woke, he willed the horses back to gray tintypes.

There was a wooded lot behind Mr. Richard's tiny square of earth, undisturbed for decades. It was thick with crisscrossed timber too spindly for anything except firewood, and far too rough to economically build on. Mr. Richard valued it as a privacy screen and for the birds it attracted—American robins, cardinals, white-breasted nuthatches, and the occasional screech owl, dozing away the day in a tree hollow. Eventually the town took the lot for delinquent taxes and auctioned it off. Mr. Richard missed the auction. His neighbor, whom he did not know, and whose house sat diagonally to the rear of Mr. Richard's, bought the abutting land for a pittance.

Mr. Richard's bantam rooster neighbor dressed himself in new, stiff logging chaps, a new, shiny hardhat, and with a new chainsaw began clear-cutting the lot. It was slow work for one man and the saw's racket rose and fell every day until dark. Whenever he successfully dropped a tree without it hanging up, the neighbor would shout, "That's what I'm talking about!" Mr. Richard watched from his kitchen window as the trees disappeared.

When the neighbor reached the trees that bordered Mr. Richard's tiny backyard, Mr. Richard took up his cane and hobbled the short distance to the property line where the man was bending over his saw, refueling it from a red gas can.

"Excuse me, neighbor," Mr. Richard said, smiling.

"Yeah?" The man stood rigidly, as if expecting a challenge.

"Are you planning to cut all the trees?"

"Yup."

"No border trees for erosion and privacy?" Mr. Richard asked, hopefully.

"Nope. Town says I can clear-cut a lot of this size, so that's just what I'm going to do."

Mr. Richard stood stooped, propped against his cane.

"Surely a few trees for privacy wouldn't make a difference?"

"When I'm done cutting and ripping stumps, I'll be trucking in fill and extending my side lawn out here. It's my land." He fished in his t-shirt pocket, stepped forward and handed Mr. Richard a business card. "That might help you out." He yanked his saw into a sputtering idle and strutted away to the next tree.

Mr. Richard looked at the card in his fingers. Built-Rite Fencing, it read.

Mr. Richard watched for a moment as his neighbor gunned the saw to cutting speed. When it bit into the next tree, a half-dozen birds exploded from its crown and shot away in different directions.

Mr. Richard watched a tiny white feather slowly spin to the ground, then hobbled back to his house.

A warm spring became a dusty summer, and true to his word, the neighbor trucked in load after load of fill. The fill was trash, and Mr. Richard looked out from his kitchen window at a badland where a few rain showers surfaced small pieces of rusty metal, bits of broken glass, and some skeletal tree roots reaching up like bony fingers. The rain also germinated the weed seeds dormant in the fill, and the lot was soon covered with crabgrass, plantain, and creeping Charlie—which quickly infiltrated Mr. Richard's yard. Mr. Richard saw his neighbor standing in his new, expanded side yard. His hands were on his hips and he looked pleased.

One morning, Mr. Richard treated himself to a diner breakfast. He sat at the counter, stirring his oily coffee. Over the clatter of silverware and sturdy plates being brought to the tables behind him, he listened to the truckers and tradesmen bantering with the counter waitress and grill cook. Some of their back-and-forth made him smile. Long ago, he would have joined in with their cheery wisecracking, but no longer. He didn't have the energy. After breakfast, he drove to a lawn and garden center.

Later, parts of the neighbor's yard curled inward, turned brown, and died. Nothing else would grow in those spots. A few weeks later, the neighbor climbed a ladder to his roof to pound down some loose shingles. When he happened to turn and look out at his savannah, he saw the clear shape of an enormous phallus painted in dead grass.

Mr. Richard peered out from behind a curtain as the neighbor stormed up and down his obscene crop circle.

"That's what I'm talking about," Mr. Richard said quietly.

Mr. Richard watched as his daughter's car pulled into the driveway. She wore a light cotton dress with a floral print and looked divinely young. He had been expecting her and had brewed coffee and put out a plate of cheap supermarket pastry, devoid of any flavor except sugar.

They sat at the kitchen table with their coffee and untouched pastry. She always smelled as if she were fresh from the shower.

After answering her father's how-are-you, how-is-work questions, she leaned forward and bore in.

"Dad, why do you do this stuff? Hobbling with that drugstore cane. You don't need that thing. When you think nobody is looking, you walk like a soldier. The guy living behind you. I heard about it. Only you would think to draw a giant penis on his lawn in weed killer."

Mr. Richard shrugged. "That whole thing back there was a mess to start. Can't prove a thing."

"Come on, Dad!"

He raised his chin and looked her in the eyes. They had the same blue-gray eyes and the mirror image always startled him a bit.

"Okay. The cane. It's so I look harmless. Let's see how people are when they think the guy at the counter is just an old man. And Paul Bunyan out back?" Mr. Richard jerked his thumb over his shoulder. "He could have been a good neighbor and at least considered some middle ground, but no. *You don't like it, old man? Go buy a fence.* Nice guy. I ate plates and plates of crap my whole life because of ... people." He spat the word. "My cheesy boss taking credit for my ideas all those years. The doctors who dismissed your mother as a hypochondriac no matter how much we argued—I argued—until she was terminal. Because I was Joe Nobody. Because I had no clout. Well, I'll have no more of it."

"That's just not healthy, Dad."

"Neither is habitually turning the other cheek. It only gets you slapped a second time."

"It's unhealthy, Dad—you sticking to yourself and this house like you do." She drummed her fingers on the table twice, her groomed nails clicking against the wood. "And your ... antics when you're offended are just plain ... malevolent."

"Malevolent. Now there's a word."

"Dad, everybody has runs of disappointment or failure. Life's always up and down. And people die—early and unfairly. You can't avenge yourself for every slight. It'll rot you from the inside." She leaned back and raised her hands in a gesture of helplessness. "Good Lord. I can't believe I'm giving lessons about adulthood to my elderly father. Shouldn't it be the other way around?"

"You know, honey, when you're young, you wait for your life to unfold, like sitting in the audience excited to see what happens when the curtain goes up. You're wide-eyed and expectant. But when you get to the end of act three, you want your money back."

"People care for you, Dad."

"Do they? When is my birthday?"

Her face colored. She looked down at her cup.

"It was last Tuesday, but who's keeping score?" he said.

"You are. Always."

"More coffee?"

"No." She stood, her chair scraping, and made for the kitchen door. She rattled the door knob, then looked back at him.

"I'm sorry I'm another disappointment," she said.

"Take some pastry."

He watched her back out of the driveway a little too fast and speed away. He told himself he should have let the forgotten birthday slide. But he didn't. Couldn't. His instinct to counterpunch was far too strong, even toward someone who cared enough to check in on him weekly.

That night, after he took an antacid tablet for a vague heartburn, he crawled into his rumpled bed in his darkened, dusty-smelling bedroom. A gust of wind rattled one of the drawn shades. They were old-fashioned, dark green shades, to keep the light out. As he lay there blinking into the darkness, all his secret regrets came and went, like strobe flashes. They made him writhe and thump the mattress with his fist.

"I've been a crybaby my whole life," he whispered into the dark. "With a mean streak. I think that may be the most honest thing I've ever said."

But then it occurred to him that it might not be too late. It's never too late. There's always a way out. A phone call. A gesture. He would call his daughter tomorrow.

That comforted him and gradually he drifted off. He dreamed of his childhood country, perfectly preserved in his memory. He stood just on the edge of endless woods. He smelled something rich and dark, familiar and comforting: forest, black dirt, rotting leaves. He looked up at tall maple trees, crowns gently circling in the wind. The wind rose higher and blew shredded clouds across the wide blue sky, then it shifted and pushed at his back, as if urging him on.

Then suddenly it was autumn in his dream forest, and every flaming leaf was an exotic dancer quaking in the breeze. He stepped forward and felt his feet sink into the soft humus. It was cool in the shade.

He looked up just ahead toward an old cart path that bisected the woods. He tossed his cane aside, marched to the path, crossed, and climbed through the broken stitchery of a collapsing buck-and-rail fence. He found himself at the edge of an ancient pasture. He stopped there at the fence, catching his breath and waiting for his fluttering heart to steady. In the center of the pasture was a colossal oak. Three compact, muscular, chestnut horses with thick black manes grazed in its shadows. He could hear the rip-rip-rip sound as they picked the best-of-the-best from the wild overgrowth. They were Morgans, these three, and one-by-one they raised their heads and began to walk toward him. The gentle drumbeat of their hooves on turf was the most gracious sound he'd ever heard.

Mr. Richard leaned back against the mossy fence and waited for them.

ILL WINDS

Sharon A. Harmon

If ill winds blow
across the landscape,
we tend to hide.
We search deep for comfort.

Keep the bone-cold at bay,
resort to another
time in our lives,
where warmth of goodness
held us sway.

Secretly pray for the glimpse
of slanted sunlight
that spans our hearts.

Heidi Larsen

WIND SPIRITS

Sharon A. Harmon

It is said that bottle trees were
believed to be spirit catchers.
The brightly-hued bottles
glowing in the sun
swaying in the breeze,
dotted the backroads of
my Southern youth.
Enticing evil spirits into them,
they protected the owner.

You entice me in that
same, radiant, mysterious
way; glowing hair and skin
nuances behind your eyes,
gleaming gold bracelets
clinking in the wind.

It is believed that when
a strong wind whips through a
bottle tree, it emits a low moan,
signifying the death of
the captive spirits.
I hear that sound and
decide I cannot let your dazzling
prisms glance off my face,
imprison me.

Previously published in Autumn Light Press, *2008*

MAMA HAD A BABY AND THE HEAD POPPED OFF

Aurynanya

Children breathe wishes
into a dandelion's cottony puff of seeds,
watching as it wafts in all directions,
spreading them for miles and miles.
Always riding the wind
to the promise of life,
somewhere new.

Another “weed” emerges
from a little crack in a concrete smile
etched into a sidewalk.
New life can almost always be found
in the hardest and most unlikely of places.
The yellow blooms
fighting, twisting, pushing toward the moon,
the sun, the stars.

Plucking it from the earth,
with its hollow stem and milky sap
you flick the flower's head off
sending it soaring into the air
all the while chanting
"Mama had a baby and the head popped off!"
just as you did when you were a child.

Such is the fate of childhood dreams.

THE MAN WITH THE RAKE

Les Clark

The beauty of Massachusetts is its scenic roads.

Among other first place finishers are its autumn colors, the busloads of leaf peepers, Old Ironsides in the Charlestown Navy Yard, the summer Cape Cod interlopers with their exclusive sandals, psychedelic shorts, designer shades, and let's not forget Fenway Park.

Down one of these picturesque Sudbury byways is the Wayside Inn, and up the slope, the Grist Mill. Beyond and further from the rude stone wall bordering the few parking spaces on the days of my visit was a flat carpet of freshly mown grass. At its upper edge spun the iconic, Depression-era, eighteen-foot blood-red water wheel rotating slowly from gravity-fed water. It is serene, almost hypnotizing.

A roughhewn fence, fronting the more imposing and (supposedly) child-proof one, holds back white puffball dandelions and a kid named Rodney, whose attempts at a juvenile high jump were successfully thwarted. I'm thinking Rodney's parents need one of those extension dog leashes.

I took the standard touristy pictures and moved up the left side path. The old world waterwheels once daily grinding wheat, corn, and other grains were the Stonehenge of milling. Some have safely fallen against the slope, like giant buttons on a grassy vest. Others, like round grave stones, still stand proudly upright. I hoped they were secure, and that Rodney wouldn't give them a push.

Depending on the desired grind quality, the wheels have dozens of slight to heavy grooves radiating from the center mounting holes—they're like rays of the sun. Some depressions are so deep an adult arm would lay in comfortably. Farmers waiting patiently, grain sacks in hand, would not appreciate someone falling into that operation.

After I climbed the stairs, I passed through a crude spring-loaded door allowing entry into the inner workings of the mill. A man was sanding a length of dowel taped to a regular steel garden rake. It looked like blue painter's tape, but it didn't split under his efforts.

"What are you doing?" I asked. *I'm often good at the obvious.*

He didn't stop. "I have to do some raking in the spillway. And I need a long reach."

"What are you raking?"

"Water chestnuts. They tend to clog everything." He stopped for a moment, and added patiently, "I just became the new miller and I have to do the raking every couple of days."

"Can I go with you when you do this?" I was thinking then of Mike Rowe and his program, *Dirty Jobs.* I quickly ducked out of the way of this jury-rigged weed grabber. *Not something to say three times fast.* I held the door for him.

"What does one put on their resume to show they want to be a miller?"

He laughed. "I'm also a contractor...a restoration specialist fixing up old buildings. I grew up around here and they know me for the work I do."

We walked along a path opposite the flow of water in the stream to our left. "See, there's that stuff."

"What is?" I asked like a rube. All I could see were pretty carpets of water-borne greenery. They were, depending on the angle, dark shades of green, yellow green and money green. "That should be easy to grab," I said ignorantly. Little did I know.

He stepped confidently onto a broad but wet flat rock, teetering with his Rube Goldberg contraption and held onto the end like a scene out of Ahab and the whale on their first meeting. With one thrust he captured a rake full. As he dragged the mass back to the steep bank, I saw just beneath the rippling water the huge lump he'd ripped from the stream bed. It looked like Medusa clumps of dripping tendrils and black seed pods.

"It's like a glacier," I offered. "Very little on the top but nine-tenths rooted to the bottom." *I watch PBS.*

"Exactly," he confirmed. And not missing a beat, he flung the rake-cum-harpoon out for another bite. Within minutes, he had a knee-high mound beside his shins. He held his hand level at his waist to show me how much higher the hill would get.

"See, these are the seed pods. They germinate underwater. It's all I can do to keep up with it. It's an invasive species. Some places it grows so thick it uses up all the oxygen and the fish die. I don't know how it all got here. Maybe Asia."

I added, "It's loosestrife and milfoil. There's other invasive plants New England deals with."

"Exactly," the man with the rake added as the most visible of the plants was now free of their muddy moorings.

"Is there any use for this stuff?"

He said, "Sudbury sends over a truck and hauls it away. It can be used for mulch because it can't germinate above ground."

"You know," I said, looking at his waste-high hillocks, "if you need another job, cleaning up after the elephant parade is just like this."

He laughed as we started talking about the demise of Ringling Brothers and reminisced about the old Boston Garden when the circus came to town. It was a great segue.

About this time I introduced myself. His name was Ben. Ben had not skipped a beat. He was stocky but muscular. His tanned face sported neatly trimmed, graying whiskers. A dozen throws, and a dozen feet closer to the water wheel, and he had only cut halfway into the untold submerged islands of water chestnuts. It was arduous work. Piles and piles along the bank attested to his sweaty efforts.

"The good thing is that in the winter it dies off."

I thought Mother Nature might have other ideas.

There were now people on the path as I walked back. I waved goodbye to Ben. As I got to the bridge by the ancient grinding wheels, I looked back. Ben was still throwing and raking—raking and throwing. I thought of Hercules and his solution for cleaning out the Aegean Stables. Ben may have a lifetime job.

As I took photos along the trails, I spied, under some weeds, tapered black scales of a snake minding its own business, possibly with a meal in its sights. I backed away because I know how I am with a three-course.

I returned to my car. The unpaved parking lot was like any other in America, strewn with plastic bottles, supermarket bags and butts.

Hey Ben, when you're done up there...

WAITING FOR SPRING

Mary J. Kellar

I can't wait for sunny days
To know that spring is on the way
I long to hear the robins sing
Then we'll know it's really spring

Birds will twitter in the trees
Seagulls on the beach fly free
Grabbing clams from spurting sands
Chasing small crabs cross the land

Watching flowers grow and bloom
Wind blows off the winter gloom
I can't wait for spring to come
Sharing cookouts and beach time fun

SUCH FIERCE WIND

Shali Sanders

Doctors said she was born
With wind in her heart,
Such fierce wind that the hinges
Would not close.
She was dressed warmly
Yet her insides shivered and
Shook her from this world early.

THE WIND AND ERICA

Emelie Rutherford

The gray goose poop should have alerted them, but they didn't know (or care) what laid between their faded beach towels and the Winsor Dam. If they cared, they wouldn't have been surrounded by dozens of webbed feet and deafening honking beaks.

"Gross, run!" Erica yelled, her auburn hair whipping across her freckled face as she stood up on the steep grassy dam. "It's a whole flock, or something, of f-ing birds. The wind brought them here!"

"Hurrrryyyyyy," Jane bellowed mere seconds later from the safety of the blue Cavalier. She half-laughed, half-hyperventilated watching Erica shoo away the Canadian geese while grabbing the radio and baby oil. Jane knew Erica didn't mind commandeering this Quabbin Reservoir escape; she'd been running the show since their kindergarten sandbox days. She even made membership cards for the Michael Jackson Fan Club in second grade.

"Oh shit, they're coming after us," Erica screamed, laughing so hard that she nearly cried as they sped away from the Quabbin.

Within seconds, of course, they heard the dreaded wail of sirens and saw strobing blue lights. Staties. A skinny clean-shaven state police officer with a tight fade pulled behind the Cavalier on Route 9, in a spot everyone knew was a speed trap.

"Oooh, he's kinda cute," Erica whispered as Jane slapped her on the knee, pausing from searching the car for incriminating plastic baggies.

"Good afternoon, miss," the officer said, the wind nearly blowing off his hat. "Do you know how fast you were going? A car like this shouldn't even be driving that fast."

"Oh, Officer, um, Thibeault, I am sooo sorry," Erica said, batting her eyelashes. The corner of the thirty-something cop's mouth turned up as his eyes fixed on Erica's tank top. "It's just that, you know, these crazy geese attacked us. And one bit me! I think it might have rabies, or something. So I need to get to the hospital before I start foaming at the mouth. Seriously, I could be really sick."

The officer flashed a concerned smile and declared, "If that's true, you really need to have that bite looked at. Do you want an escort to the hospital?"

"Oh no, we're OK. But thank you," Erica said, holding her hand to her face.

As soon as the now-grinning officer turned to walk to his cruiser Erica peeled away.

"Sucker!" Erica hooted, giving Jane a high-five. "So, what's Plan B? Where can we lay out?"

"I dunno. Should we just give up? Maybe we can't get a good tan today, anyway, because it's wicked windy," Jane said.

"Bullshit," Erica declared—convincing and comforting her timid sidekick. "The sun's still the sun. Let's head back to town." The girls started scheming, searching for anyone with a pool, or even yard, they could hijack for sunbathing. No luck. If only Jane's older brother wouldn't heckle them if they laid out on their deck, or if Erica had a yard. Resigned, and accepting that it *was* really windy, they drove around town all afternoon drinking peach Schnapps and skunked Natural Light. Jane talked about her fears of attending Brown in the fall, and Erica schemed to make enough money as a nanny to visit her at least once a month. Jane was already glum, thinking she wouldn't see Erica every day, starting in only a few short months.

Erica was striking. She had thick curly hair and resembled a younger Paula Abdul, their teachers said. She was the star athlete, prom queen, and Jane's best friend. And she was funny—could tell dirty jokes that made even her dad's hunter buddies snort. Jane—plain Jane with the short legs and boring straight hair—hadn't seen Erica since the summer after high school. That was decades ago, before college, responsibility, and life outside of New England.

Now, present-day grown-up Jane, standing in the laundry aisle at the grocery store, back home in Massachusetts, can't stop thinking about the Quabbin goose poop. Goose poop! So many more poignant memories existed that Jane could have recalled, tied to hot chocolate at Wachusett, vomit in their older friends' dorm rooms, white lies at Family Planning, closed caskets in Charboneau Funeral Home … Still, that goose poop is what dominates Jane's mind as she hides from a grown-up "Erica" and her outdoorsy-looking husband (boyfriend?) in their perfect Patagonia gear. This couple is one aisle away from Jane in Big Y, the store Jane and Erica's friends would meet near to find beer-buyers in high school, when no one wore Patagonia. Jane knows rationally that the person she just saw can't be Erica, but the resemblance is so striking that she's overwhelmed by cognitive dissonance, temporary insanity, something she doesn't understand. One thing she does know is that she can't be near this duo.

Once the coast is clear, Jane limps out of the grocery store, pulling on her hood to block the Arctic blast the *Telegram & Gazette* warned readers about. She drives her rental car toward her brother's house—their former childhood home. But she doesn't make it. The wind makes her think more about that goose attack day and others like it. So much longing and partying and cavorting in this town. So much Erica. She wants more. She imagines she's in a Lifetime movie about reconnecting with a long-lost friend and community. She drives back to Big Y as the wind whips snow flurries on the windshield.

"Excuse me," Jane says in an almost panicked tone at the Customer Service counter, her hands trembling inexplicably in her pockets. "I grew up here and thought for a moment I saw an old friend. Did you know her, or maybe where her dad lives now?"

The squat woman with the face mole and pageboy haircut hasn't heard of Erica. No one in Customer Service has. She leans against the Kolaczki cookie display for support, frantically searching Facebook on her iPhone. No Erica. Jane looks at the Polish desserts and feels an overwhelming need she can't pinpoint. She pops a Xanax and wanders the aisles, ignoring the nagging pain in her leg. The deli counter, snack aisle, and bakery all stir up memories of childhood and Erica. Good memories. Jane pops more Xanax. She sees familiar faces—mainly relatives of old high school friends—and exchanges small pleasantries with them. She has fun, in her mind. She leaves Big Y and ponders hitting Gabe's for a beer or three, but decides against it. After such a rollercoaster of a day, if she actually did see Erica's dad, how would she act?

The wind is strong, and it sways the rental as Jane drives up Temple Street. When she turns into the driveway, her brother jogs out of the house.

"We better hurry," he says, hopping in the passenger seat and giving Jane a hug. "The anniversary mass for Erica starts soon."

"I know. Sorry, my bad for being MIA today. I honestly kinda lost it today. I seriously thought I saw Erica at Big Y. I started questioning if it was all real. I've been off my meds and my mind was playing tricks on me. It's so weird to think the accident was twenty years ago. It seriously never gets easier."

They drive down the hill toward the only remaining Catholic church in town. Jane closes her eyes, and for one final moment lets herself believe Erica is really out there, fighting off geese, state troopers, and all the perils in the world.

WIND SONG

THE DOE

Diane Hinckley

"There's worse places than Chernobyl," Bernie Shelton mumbled into his beer. The barroom door banged open, punctuating Bernie's remark.

Bill Latham slid off the bar stool and slammed the door shut. You had to slam it or the wind would suck it open again. No one spoke in answer to Bernie's curious pronouncement. They'd been watching something on the TV about Russian soldiers mindlessly digging trenches at Chernobyl. Probably all those soldiers would get cancer if they didn't get killed in the war. Bill, who'd been in two wars, didn't know which was worse. He hadn't had cancer yet.

Finally, out of politeness more than anything, Roger LeBlanc acknowledged Bernie's statement. "Yeah?"

"Windy night like this reminds me. I went hunting once out on Bemis Hill Road, behind what used to be the Gilford place."

"The meth house?" The house had exploded the year before, killing two inhabitants. They weren't local people, and no one mourned them.

"This was a while back, after old lady Gilford finally died and nobody was living there."

"Oh," said Roger, "I never went hunting out there."

"Nobody did, that I know of. Nobody ever went out there. I mean, it was posted with 'No Trespassing' signs, but nobody gave a rat's ass about that. There was nobody around to see you going in there, and old Lovelock, the game warden, didn't even go in there."

"Kids must've gone back there," Ed Bingley said. "We were always running around the woods behind the cemetery, lighting swamp gas with cigarette lighters and falling into cellar holes."

"Lovelock once caught my old man and me jacking deer," said Bill, hoping to change the subject. He didn't like to hear talk about the stretch of woods behind the Gilford house.

"None of you went out in those woods when you were kids, did you?" challenged Bernie. Nobody answered.

The door slammed open again, and Bill went over and

slammed it so hard it startled the others. He remembered the kids' talk, about those woods being cursed, about Old Lady Gilford being a witch. He'd never taken it seriously. If any place was cursed, it was his family's overcrowded little house, with Dad always carrying on about his time in Vietnam and about how if you hadn't been a "warrior" you were no kind of man. Well, Bill had been a warrior, and then he'd been in the woods behind the Gilford house.

"That wind was the damnedest thing," said Bernie. "The air was bone still until I got in the woods, quite a ways out there. I usually like some wind, so the animals can't catch my scent."

Ed started to say something but chuckled into his beer instead.

"I was standing almost on the edge of the swamp, and this deer walks right in front of me. It was a doe, and I lifted my shotgun, and the wind almost pulled me over sideways. I swear it yanked that gun to the left, just as I got off the shot."

"Buck fever," opined Roger.

"Doe fever," quipped Ed. "You got a doe permit, Bern?"

"Like I told you, you ain't going to see no game warden out there."

"Hey, Bill," asked Roger. "You ever go out there, behind the Gilford house?"

Yes, he had. He'd been bow hunting. The wind had started as soon as the doe crossed his path. He'd felt something like a giant's hand pulling his bow to the left. But he'd learned a lot when out hunting as a kid, and he'd learned a lot in places like Fallujah. He pulled the bow up and to the right and fired the arrow.

"Bill?" Roger was looking at him with concern.

"Anyways," said Bernie. "I got this weird feeling, a feeling I didn't even know a name for. It was like these evil fingers was trying to open a door into my soul."

"Oh, come on," Ed roared. "That was your colonoscopy."

"I never believed those stories," Bernie snapped. "That's why I was there. But you go to a place like that, you wisht you was in Chernobyl, digging trenches."

"Don't have a meltdown, Bern. I thought you were joking." Talons of windblown sand scrabbled against the window, and the blue neon Old Dana Road Beer sign fluttered and dipped.

Bill went to sit in one of the empty booths and laid both his hands on the sticky table, palms down. The others kept talking but it was just background noise, like the TV that was showing exploded apartments in a foreign city. He wanted to leave but thought maybe he'd better rest awhile. He'd hardly had anything to drink, but he didn't feel like he should drive.

Back in those woods behind the Gilford house, when he let the arrow fly it hit the deer, but not where he was aiming. He got her in the rear left haunch. She hobbled off with the arrow still sticking out of her, leaving a trail of blood spots. Oh, damn, he thought, this was the worst thing: wounding an animal and not killing it, leaving it to suffer.

He took off after the deer as she limped through the woods. After a while he couldn't see her, but he could see the spots of red in the snow. The merciless wind made his nose run. He'd walked into the woods in perfect November conditions—an inch of snow on the ground for easy tracking and the air not too snappy. Now his hands were tingling, even as his body was sweating from the chase.

He passed from running to trudging, but he never lost the hoof tracks or the blood spots. He wanted to finish off the doe before he got too far from the road. He'd have to haul out the carcass, and he'd want to do it before dark.

"Hey, Bill, you okay over there?" asked Roger. Bill jumped, his eyes swerving in Roger's direction. Over Roger's head, the television showed zombie tanks churning through mud. On each tank was a big white Z.

Out in the frozen, wind-tormented woods, he'd lost feeling in his feet, but he kept trudging until he found himself in a little clearing around a tar paper shack. Smoke twisted out of the chimney, joining the growing mass of troubled clouds. Bill had thought no one lived out in the woods anymore. Tar paper shacks had gone the way of single-wide trailers as suburban types moved in and took over town government, making new rules.

A woman came out from behind the woodpile, her arms laden with wood. She wore a brown wool cap from which an auburn braid snaked out. Animated by the wind, it curled and twisted like an angry viper. "You'd better come in out of the wind," she said. Her voice was a low rasp nearly covered by the waterfall sound of a forest fighting to stay upright.

Bill forced his frozen mouth to form words. "I have to find

the doe. She's wounded."

"You'll die of hypothermia if you don't come in," she said. She opened the door for him and followed him inside. She tossed the wood onto the floor, where it clattered and rolled beside the stove.

Bill tried to express his thanks, but the words came out slow and drunk-sounding. The wind banged against the shack. He dropped into a wooden chair next to a scabrous table as his feet started to thaw, painfully waking the nerves.

The woman put a cup of tea in front of Bill, and he clutched it for warmth. She sat opposite him, lowering into the chair stiffly, as though she were lame on one side. Her face was young and serene, belying the bodily stiffness that twisted her body like that of a crone. He wondered how she would look with her hair flowing free. He pictured the tendrils of hair whipping around in the cold wind. "I think you saved my life," he said.

"Yes, I did."

"As soon as I've warmed up, I'll have to go after that doe. She's wounded, and I have to finish her off."

"Don't worry about the doe," she said, looking at him with blank yet wary yellow-brown eyes. He'd seen that sharp but absent look in the eyes of a bear he'd met on the old cart road behind his house. The bear had stared for a while, then turned aside and melted into the woods.

"I can't leave that deer to suffer," he said.

"Why not?" she said. "We all suffer. You suffer. I left those two men to suffer."

"Two men?"

"At the Gilford house. They were on my land. They didn't die right away."

"I'm on your land," Bill said. "I didn't mean to trespass."

"Yes, you did. And you meant to kill the doe. And your aim was true, as true as it could be in the wind. So as a reward I'm going to let you suffer."

Bill blundered out the door, into the snow. In front of the shack, in a red mess of snow, was the arrow. He pushed his way through the woods, following his own tracks, sweating and freezing, until at dusk he came out to the place where he'd parked his truck.

"Bill?"

Bill looked up at Roger, seeing worry in the man's eyes.

“Gotta go,” Bill said. “Tomorrow’s a workday.” He gave the door a good slam on his way out.

HOW WE MADE A BIRDHOUSE SO THE BIRDS COULD BE HAPPY

Amanda Russell

As impenetrable as the song of an oriole
rising over distance from a thicket, out of season,
on replay in the hour before sleep—
memory is that mirror showing all things as they aren't.
It cannot speak without a mouth reflected in it.
It cannot see without my eyes claiming it as residence
where I tease out what is knotted
and follow it into relevance.

I remember my daughter
practicing the *jeté* before riding
a stickered stick horse to bed,
sporting a reflective crown and mismatched
shoes: one plastic high heel and one
Elmo slipper. I remember the separate sounds of each
kicked off before sleep. I remember
I sang to her. I remember also my son

climbing walls and dressers, slamming doors
and enjoying the moments we washed windows together,
our faces in reflection, how much better we could see
the milk carton we'd painted. And cut. And hung
in the maple as a home for the birds so the birds could be happy.

I see it still, before sleep. Tilting. Twirling
in the wind. Seeking spring amid snow.

NATURE SPEAKS

Ellie Burton

Nature speaks,
as long as you listen.

She sends messages
through birdsong,
wind gusts,
flowers,
and stars.

The birds' melodies carry her songs
in lively symphonies,
the wind gusts carry her secrets
through the forest,
the flowers carry her love notes
in their petals and sweet scents,
and the stars carry her wisdom
in sacred arrangements.

Her messages are
everywhere.
We just need to stop–
long enough to hear them.

NIGHT OF WIND

Heidi Larsen

I lay here sleeping, well, not quite,
My head filled with uncertain fright.
These winds of change blow oft too strong,
And storm winds circle unduly long.

Currents are young; therefore, am I.
Hurricanes growing, rolling by.
Whispering secrets which lie ahead
Yet, there is safety in my own bed.

Bed means comfort, sheets fresh and new;
A haven of safety from looming adieu.
The tempest tosses, adventures unknown,
But impending change is too frightful a tone.

I'll wait in my bed, riding the endless night.
Soaring through dreams, then ceasing my flight.
Where I land, I shall not know.
Storm winds shall determine their blow.

AS THE SCARECROW FLIES

Kathy Chencharik

BANG! BANG! BANG! Twelve-year-old Cindy jolted awake. She sat up in bed, glanced toward her upstairs bedroom window, and watched as the wind sent leaves and debris dancing through the gray morning light. BANG! BANG! BANG! There it was again. She saw what looked like a dark brown glove beating against the window pane. *Something must have gotten stuck on the shutters,* she thought, getting out of bed. At the window, she looked down and noticed a scarecrow attached to the brown glove. It twisted and turned in the wind. Cindy opened the window. Her long blonde hair blew across her face as she yanked on the glove, releasing it from the shutter. She began to pull, and once it was halfway inside the scarecrow opened its eyes, looked up and said, "Thank you."

Cindy screamed and let go. The wind picked up, taking the straw man with it. She took a few deep breaths to calm herself, leaned out the window, and watched as the scarecrow did a few loop-de-loops through the air. It flew toward the top of their big red barn and soon became snagged on the horse-shaped weathervane. The horse and rider spun around twice. The scarecrow's arm came up in a wave, reminding Cindy of a rodeo she'd once seen on TV. Once free again, it flew from the barn and soon disappeared from view. Cindy closed the window, put on a sweatshirt, jeans, and sneakers, and hurried downstairs.

"It's about time you got up, sleepyhead," her mother said, watching as her daughter took a seat at the kitchen table. "Your breakfast is getting cold," she continued as she set a plate of bacon and eggs in front of her.

Cindy glanced at her younger brother, Tommy, as he stuffed scrambled eggs into his mouth. He looked at her and laughed. She almost gagged at the cavernous egg-filled mouth. "That's gross, Tommy."

She turned away from him and looked at her mother. "I'm so late because there was a scarecrow outside my bedroom window."

Tommy howled with laughter as eggs fell from his mouth like fat yellow raindrops.

"Stop that, Tommy," their mother said, trying her best not to laugh. Then she turned to Cindy and said, "I believe that's the best excuse I've heard so far. I'll have to tell your father that one, or better yet, you can. He's going to need your help outside after you've finished breakfast. We're in for a nor'easter."

"Can I go out and help too?" Tommy asked.

"No," their mother said. "I need your help inside today."

"It's not an excuse," Cindy insisted. "It's true. There was a scarecrow, and he talked to me!"

Tommy laughed so hard that tears streamed down his face. Their mother handed him a tissue, then placed a hand on Cindy's forehead. "Maybe you'd better stay inside. I think you may have a fever. Either that or you were dreaming."

Cindy knew her parents wouldn't believe her. They always said she had an overactive imagination. "I'm fine," she said, pushing her mother's hand away. "But I think you're right, Mom; it must have been a dream."

"That's more like it. Now finish your breakfast and go help your father."

Cindy ate in silence. When she finished, she pushed her chair back and stood up.

"Boo!" Tommy shouted as he danced around her. "I'm a scarecrow!"

"Grow up," Cindy said as she headed for the door.

"Better put on a raincoat," her mother called.

Cindy stopped at the coat rack in the hallway. She grabbed her bright red raincoat, slipped into it, then headed to the barn. Yellow, orange, and red leaves from the many trees surrounding their farm covered the yard like a blanket, crunching beneath her sneakers. She searched the sky for the flying scarecrow. The leaves swirled, twirled, and danced around her in the wind, but the scarecrow was nowhere in sight. *Maybe it had been a dream after all*, she thought. Cindy scanned the yard and saw her father entering the barn. At the same time, she felt the first drop of rain and raised her hood. She helped her father tie everything down. After they got the animals safely inside the barn they returned to the house to ride out the storm.

By nightfall the wind had begun to subside, and the rain had stopped.

"Is the storm over, Daddy?" Cindy asked as her father kissed her goodnight. She thought about telling him about the scarecrow but decided against it. Whatever it was, it was gone now.

"This storm is. But another is predicted for the day after tomorrow. Seems like every year, the storms get stronger. They canceled school on Monday because of it. You were a big help today. Thanks. Now get some sleep."

"Goodnight, Daddy. Don't worry; I can help with the next one, too."

* * *

The next morning, Cindy went out behind the barn to check on her pumpkin patch. As she walked along the narrow dirt lane she sniffed the air, loving the scents of autumn. Above her was a canopy of sunlit golden leaves, and quite a few birch trees had been bent over from Saturday's strong winds. At the pumpkin patch, she was relieved to see that most had stood their ground. However, some had been uprooted, smashed and tossed about by the storm. She stood in the middle, surveying the damage, and tried to decide which pumpkin she wanted to carve for Halloween.

"Oh, little girl," came a voice from behind.

Cindy jumped, spun around, and scanned the tree-lined stone wall surrounding the garden. "Hello? Is someone out there?"

"Up here," said the voice. "I'm stuck in this tree."

Cindy felt a slight tap on her shoulder. She looked and noticed an old boot with a blue top. Glancing up, she saw the scarecrow. It was dangling from a tree branch, swaying in the gentle breeze.

Cindy backed away. "You're not there. You're just a fig mint of my imagination."

"I believe that's a figment."

"My parents are right. I do have an overactive imagination."

"Well, I hate to disagree with them, but a figment or not, I am stuck up here. Could you please help me? Why did you let me go yesterday? You almost had me inside."

"I wasn't dreaming?" Cindy asked as she climbed onto the wall, reached up and released the scarecrow from the branch.

"Dreaming?" The scarecrow fell, plopping next to Cindy, straw puffing out from his shirt.

"Yes," she said as she pulled pieces of straw from her hair. "My mother told me I must have been dreaming, and I believed her."

"Why?"

"Because scarecrows can't talk."

"Oh? Who told you that?"

"No one has to tell me. Scarecrows are made of straw and old clothes. They aren't real. Besides, the only scarecrow I know who can talk is the one in that old movie, The Wizard of . . ."

"Oz," the scarecrow finished.

"Yeah. That's the one. It's on TV again tonight, and he didn't have a brain."

"Well, I do. I was in the original movie, a real straw-stuffed scarecrow. However, Hollywood has decided to make a remake of it. As it turns out, the woman who plays the part of the Wicked Witch of the West is a real witch. During rehearsal, she cast a spell on me. Now I'm more like a man than a scarecrow. But the good thing is I don't feel pain like a real man would."

"So, how did you end up here?"

"We were filming the remake in Kansas once again. Dorothy, her little dog Toto, and I were on the set when a real tornado came through, picking the three of us up. It carried me and dropped me here. The last I remember, the dark funnel cloud was gone, and the winds kept me flying everywhere." The scarecrow stuffed straw into his shirt as he got off the wall. "By the way, where is here?"

"New England. North Central Massachusetts."

"Thanks for helping me," he said. "Now, if I can only use my brain to find a way to get back home." He raised an arm and scratched the back of his old pointed blue hat.

"You could return the same way you came," Cindy said.

"What do you mean?"

"My dad said another nor'easter is due again tomorrow. The winds will be stronger than yesterday."

"Yes! Yes!" The scarecrow shouted as he did a little jig. "If we can find out the wind direction, and if I can get up high enough, that might do it. It may be enough to get me back."

Cindy watched the scarecrow dance and giggled at the sight.

"Do you have a computer?" the scarecrow asked.

"Of course. Why?"

"Well, if you could get me a print-out of the local and national weather forecasts, I'd be able to chart a course."

Cindy nodded. "The weathervane on top of the barn would be

the highest point."

"Oh yeah, I remember I took a little spin on that horse. Would you be able to get me back up there when the time comes?"

"Sure. No problem." Cindy jumped down from the stone wall and stood beside the scarecrow. She spotted a broken fence, walked over to it, and pulled out two boards.

"What are those for?"

"You'll see," she said as she picked up a rusty nail that had fallen out. She placed the boards in the shape of a cross, picked up a rock and pounded the nail into the boards. "You'd better stay here until I get back," she said as she carried the cross into the middle of the pumpkin patch and pushed one end down into the soft earth. "I doubt anyone will come here, but if they do, stand in front of this with your arms raised."

He looked at her askance.

"There's nothing suspicious about a scarecrow in a garden," she explained.

"And here I thought I was the one with the brain," the scarecrow said as he glanced around at the fall foliage. "It sure is pretty around here. If it doesn't work and I don't make it home for some reason, it wouldn't be so bad if I stayed here. You could be my new Dorothy. Do you have a dog?"

"No. Unfortunately, I have a little brother."

"Oh, brother," the scarecrow said with a laugh. "You don't sound too enthused."

"I'd rather have a dog." Cindy picked out a pumpkin and then started on the path toward home. "I'll be back soon with the information." She turned a corner and bumped smack dab into her little brother.

"Who are you talkin' to?" Tommy asked.

"Nobody."

"Were too."

"Were not."

"I heard you."

"Okay. If you must know, I was talking to myself."

"Really? I thought I heard someone else." Tommy started to turn the corner.

"Where are you going?" Cindy asked, trying to change the subject.

"To get a pumpkin."

"Here," she said, handing him the one she wanted. "I got this for you."

"Gee, thanks."

"Come on; I'll race you home."

Later that afternoon, Cindy returned to the pumpkin patch with a printout. She started to laugh when she saw the scarecrow standing in front of the cross with his arms raised.

"Whew. It's only you." The scarecrow lowered his arms and glanced up at the sky. Dark gray clouds were starting to form. "Do you think you could meet me at the barn at sunset?" he asked as he studied the printout. "The storm will be here earlier than your father expected."

Cindy nodded.

During supper, Cindy looked at her father and said, "You look tired. You've got everything secured for the storm tomorrow. Why don't you stay in tonight? I can bring the animals into the barn and milk the cow."

Her father raised an eyebrow. "Okay," he said. "What is it you want?"

"Nothing. I want to help."

"That's very sweet of you," her mother said. "Your father could use a break."

"It's settled then," Cindy said, getting up from the table. She carried her dishes over to the sink and glanced out the window. The trees outside swayed in the breeze, and the sun slowly sank into the darkening sky. "I'd best get going. The wind is picking up."

"Be careful," her father said. "Don't be too long."

"And put your raincoat on," her mother added.

Cindy met the scarecrow out behind the barn. With his help, she brought the animals inside and showed him how to milk a cow. A big gust of wind blew open the barn door. Then it slammed itself shut. "Follow me," she said as she led the scarecrow to a ladder. They climbed up into a hayloft. Once in the hayloft, another ladder led to the barn roof. Cindy ascended the next ladder, opened a hatch and climbed outside.

"Thank you," the scarecrow said as he climbed out after her and retook a seat on the horse. Another gust of wind buffeted them. She grabbed hold of the weathervane and clung to it.

"Hey. What's that scarecrow doin' out here?"

Cindy spun around and saw Tommy's head poking out from the hatch.

"Tommy," she scolded. "Get down now, or I'll tell mom. You know you aren't supposed to be up here."

"Neither are you," Tommy shot back. "Is that the scarecrow you were talkin' about yesterday? What's he doin' up here?"

"Getting ready to go home," the scarecrow said.

Tommy's jaw dropped. His eyes widened, and his mouth hung open as he climbed onto the roof to join them. "Wow. He really does talk."

"Get back inside. Now!" Cindy ordered as another gust of wind nearly knocked her over. She bumped into her brother. Tommy lost his balance, fell, and slid down the roof.

"Tommy! No!" she screamed into the wind as she tried to grab him. She missed.

Tommy put his feet out first, and his sneakers slowed him down as he stopped on a gutter near the edge.

The scarecrow jumped off the weathervane. "Cindy," he said. "Grab my boots and lower me down."

As she lowered the scarecrow, Cindy heard a loud roaring sound like a train. She glanced up to see a funnel cloud headed toward them. Inside, she could see two blinking red lights. The funnel stopped beside Tommy. An arm emerged through the cloud, reached out, and pulled Tommy to safety, setting him back down next to his sister. Cindy could have sworn she heard a small dog barking as the arm reached out again, grabbed the scarecrow, and pulled him inside. The funnel cloud rose, changed direction, and headed west.

* * *

"There's no place like home. There's no place like home," a girl's voice kept repeating.

"Wake up, Honey; the movie is almost over."

"Huh?" Cindy sat up, rubbed her eyes, and looked at the TV. Dorothy was talking and clicking her ruby-red shoes. "Where is Tommy?"

"In bed, asleep like you should be."

* * *

Since the scarecrow incident, Cindy had bribed her brother to keep him from telling her parents about what had happened. They had even gotten closer because of it. In October of the following year, Cindy's parents took her and her little brother into town to see the remake of 'The Wizard of Oz.' On the ride home, Cindy and Tommy sat in the backseat listening to their parents discuss the movie.

"How odd," their father said. "Cindy the Cowardly Lioness?"

"And what about Tommy the Tin Man?" her mother added. "Why can't they leave well enough alone?"

Tommy looked at Cindy. She looked at him. They both smiled and then laughed before breaking out in song. "Somewhere over the rainbow..."

BITTERSWEET

Marsha LaCroix

New growth sprouts swiftly from the soil.
Recently hacked off bittersweet regains its stature.
Knee-high tendrils innocently wave in the breeze.
I stand mesmerized, watching it sway to and fro.
I begin to walk away then turn back
Observing as the waltz continues.
Tentacles upright, tilting forward,
Undulating toward the shade of a lone maple tree.
Like waking zombies toward their victim.

Marcia LaCroix

NATURE IS HER NAME

Ellie Burton

There is a woman that everyone knows.
Her hair, an engulfing emerald green.
Her skin, a golden, caramel-brown.
Her beauty, a star that shines in the darkest night.
Her temper, is fuel to fire but also the water that washes it away.

She cannot talk, but is always speaking.
She has no ears, but is always listening.
She has no sight, but is always watching.

She dances with the wind, through the leaves of the trees:
her arms wave as the air sweeps through her
and her hips sway from side to side,
though her feet remain still— planted where they stand.

Mother,
Nature,
Necromancer,
She is all that is.

FORGOTTEN TOWN

Sharon A. Harmon

Scraggly witch trees on river banks
leeches towards a molten river.
Runs trash-filled by
empty cold factories in this
desolate town.
Broken sidewalks with weeds
growing in cracks.
And boarded-up, silent stores
with the gloom of failure
hangs in the air.
A scrawny dog whimpers
hidden in the shadows.
What secrets lie beneath this township,
coursing through the water supply?
On starless nights,
what forlorn images
in the wind-blown sky above
are whispered on hallowed nights?

SEPTEMBER

Kathy Bennett

September
Whispers through the treetops
All its summer secrets.

Leaves, shocked from their green,
Spill down to the earth
Like confidences loosed.

September skips across the sky;
O summer, don't go . . . but crispness ushers on;
Falling,
Falling,
Falling from its humid embrace,
Recalling
Those things that flamed the soul.

Fevered bellows fanning
From the season of tempest minibursts
Somehow mellowed,
Somehow fading.
September embers, now a faint whisper.

The wind whirls
And I miss listening to you.
Are you trying to call me?

The wind swirls the leaves,
Capturing my attention;
Leaving me captive—are you there?
Wild motions of air *emoting*
Whip and whisk bygone leaves
All around. Dizzying

Is their dance.
Chaotic
Is my mind.
Do you care?

Somehow mellowed,
Somehow faded.
September embers
Now a faint whisper.

THE OTHER SIDE OF THE RAINBOW

Steven Michaels

Ocknee lived in fear of the witch. Actually they all did. And how could they not? The tallest of the Munchkins was only four feet tall, while the witch had to be at least five two. Add to that her imposing stature and high heeled shoes and she was a near hulking, brooding giant living among them.

Of course, to many a Munchkin she was not so terrible. In fact, she lived in a modest sized cottage at the edge of the woods, unlike her sister who flaunted her authority in a dark and sinister castle to the west. There seemed to be no advantages to living under that witch, as many of her minions were mindless slaves. Sadly, the Munchkins were also slaves, but the majority of them seemed to prefer their life that way. Ocknee, however, thought it unbearable.

"Don't you understand?" he pleaded with his neighbors. "She's a witch and a tyrant. If we disobey, she enjoys punishing us with evil enchantments."

"Just because you cut yourself shaving doesn't mean she's cursed your razor blades," sighed Ropilda, Oknee's neighbor who often had to listen to him complain while she hung out her laundry.

"Well, that still doesn't excuse what she did to that Nick Chopper fellow! Dismembered by his own ax and now he's an unmovable hunk of tin. I tell you, she needs to be stopped!"

"You forget, *he* was trying to shack up with her maid," Ropilda reminded him. "You ask me, he had it coming. It's better if we just do as we are told so no one gets hurt."

"That's not good enough! Aren't you outraged?" seethed Ocknee.

"Look, Ocknee, we can't *all* live in an emerald city."

Ropilda may have had a point, but Ocknee refused to remain so small-minded.

"Listen, Ock," she sighed, making her way back inside, "don't make a big deal of it. She's a witch and no good can come from trying to get rid of her. I'm pretty sure her curses will outlive her."

Ocknee did value Ropilda's opinions. They had grown up

together under this tyrant after all. Unfortunately, this reminded him that the witch had been ruler for far *too* long. Painfully, he remembered how he had been drafted to fight in the war with the wizard only six years ago. Fresh out of Philpot Glurken High School, he was asked to sacrifice himself against an emerald-clad army of what could only be described as a brute squad due to their extra height advantage. It would be one thing if that wizard was looking to liberate them and start the revolution that he himself had once tried to organize. Sadly, no one seemed interested in that either.

"Why should we want to side with this wizard?" asked Murkley, another Munchkin who also suffered while listening to Ocknee's complaints. "He's an outsider!"

"But he's young! He's different! He's been places! *And* he's intelligent! I heard he donates brains and other vital organs."

"Whose brains? And to whom?"

"I don't know exactly, but–"

"You ask me, this wizard's just dangerous. I hear he calls himself all powerful. I don't buy it. He's not a witch. *They* have the *real* power here and you know it!"

In retrospect, it appeared that Ocknee had little success in stirring the imaginations of his people. To them everything was in black and white. There was only good or bad and even their definition of wicked didn't seem to measure up because they continued to live out their pathetic existence under the reign of someone they knew was evil.

Better the witch you know than the one you don't had been his mother's constant turn of phrase. But he didn't know the witch. He'd never met her. A lot of her demands were funneled down through a committee of elders who enforced all manner of decrees. And Ocknee hated her decrees. She had given them a curfew, for goodness sake. Well, she called them noise ordinances, but any raucous laughter after nine pm could end up turning a person to stone.

No. He knew enough about her to comprehend she was totally wicked. After all, she used it in her own title. And he just knew she enjoyed being evil. He could tell. Not to mention it was very clear in Oz: bad witches were ugly. She had the face of an old crone when she was only twenty eight, and it had *not* gotten better with age.

As such, the more Ocknee thought about things, he realized he needed to take matters into his own hands. He had already tried writing letters to the witches of the north and south, and they quickly responded:

> *Dear Sir or Madam,*
>
> *We are unable at this time to overpower the witches of the east and west. We do appreciate your need for service and hope you will think of us for further magical assistance, should the need arise.*
>
> *Sincerely,*
> *The North/South Good Witch Co.*

This was just as well, as Ocknee had heard the witch of the north was just some old bat who may or may not have had some sort of reconstructive surgery to ensure that she was a "good witch."

Regardless, Ocknee had been formulating a plan. He had heard of a spellbook belonging to the witch. He believed if he could just access the book he could use her own spells against her. He just needed her out of the cottage. Ocknee set about bribing the town cobbler into having a shoe sale for the witch. She really did have an unhealthy obsession with shoes. This would keep her occupied long enough while he broke into her house.

When he arrived, the witch's maid was still so distracted over the loss of her lover that she didn't even look up from her chores as Ocknee waltzed inside. Over the fireplace stood a mesmerizing book. He was sure this was it. He nimbly grabbed it off its shelf and ran from the premises. The maid barely looked up, seemingly morose in her mourning, but in truth she had been magically sedated due to her recent transgressions against the witch.

Meanwhile, Ocknee cackled with wicked glee at his thievery. He bounded to his home, ignored his mother's inquiries as to why he was home so early from his meeting with the Guild of Sweets, and ran up to his room to pour over the forbidden tome.

"There must be something in here that can blow that witch to hell!" seethed Ocknee to himself as he furiously thumbed through pages of spells like living powder formulas, anti-melting charms, and even gingerbread house recipes. There were also lots of methods of mind-control, specifically for Munchkins and other "lesser denizens of Oz," as the book addressed them.

Then on page 1900 there appeared a spell that Ocknee soon convinced himself would work. It read: "How to Summon a Gale." Admittedly, it could have easily been read as "girl" due to the intricate and ancient font of the book. Nevertheless, the spell seemed to promise the production of forceful winds capable of uprooting the witch from her very existence. Sadly, Ocknee struggled to understand the exact directions. In his fervor at the prospect of this spell, all Ocknee could really make out of the text was that a "hurricane or tornado-like effect could usher forth the destruction of the wicked." Ocknee could not be sure if this were some sort of warning against using said spell, but he assumed that such a warning would only be geared towards witches attempting such dark art. Moreover, he completely ignored the book's reasoning for summoning a gale/girl which had something to do with rejuvenating one's youth, provided you could steal the gale/girl's essence.

Barring all that nonsense, Ocknee uttered the spell:

"La frankum Baumum, Walla Denslow.
Em jee em, un toto barkum.
Howling winds please hear my cry!
Pray no witches have to die!
But if they must, let ends be quick so!
Em jee em, un toto tu oh."

Then silence.

Ocknee waited. Nothing happened. There was no wind of any sort. *Damn,* he thought. *How useless!* Why did he think such spells would work for the likes of him? The book was very clear that he was a lesser being of no value in this supposed enchanted land. In his rage, he threw the book out his bedroom window. Coincidentally, as it landed there was a thunderous crash. It felt like an earthquake! Did he destroy the book? No. Was this the spell? He stared out the window to discover a bizarre house standing in the field leading to the witch's cottage. What on Oz had just happened?

Soon all the Munchkins were gathered outside, cautiously, of course, as the likes of this house had never been seen in this land. It was huge but worn down, and not just because it fell from the sky.

Three of the Munchkins of the Elder Committee stepped forward to investigate. It was instantly declared a crime scene when the legs of the witch were discovered just under the collapsing porch of the house. At the prospect of a possible magicide, they immediately notified the North/South Witch Company. And in a near instant, the aforementioned old bat came sailing through the clouds.

Meanwhile Ocknee could hardly believe what was happening. Had he really caused this? Oddly enough, he went into shock, unable to utter a word—something entirely rare for him since most Munchkins were notoriously good at small talk. Watching the events unfold, Ocknee bordered on madness; giddy at the prospect of his success, he set about announcing his victory.

And then it happened.

A young girl of un-Ozly origin appeared in the house's doorway. She wore a shabby checkered dress covered in a fine sepia colored dust that woefully exuded how she came from a foreign and desolate wasteland. This aura, combined with her stout and hearty stature, spoke of a power yet to be ascertained as she stood there staring in detached bewilderment upon the entire assemblage.

"This is most strange," whispered the Witch to the three elders. "You were right to call me. This creature appearing from the sky can only mean she is a sorceress, much like me. Say nothing. I will handle this."

The old witch then approached the girl and bowed low. She proceeded to thank her for murdering the other witch and liberating the Munchkins from their bondage. At this, the girl looked as confused as Ocknee, and when she explained that she was not at all responsible for the killing, the old witch laughed saying her house certainly did kill the witch and that was the same thing.

"What? NO!" screamed Ocknee. The others, mistaking his enormous hollering for celebratory rioting soon began cheering and yelping in victory.

"NO! NO!' cried Ocknee. "It was ME! I summoned her! I killed the witch! It was me! ME! Do you hear? It was me! Ocknee!"

But it was too late; all his shouts were overpowered by the merriment of the crowd. Meanwhile, the old witch continued to talk to the stranger, taking her by the hand and carefully removing her from the rabble. The old witch, in her authority, was making it abundantly clear that a foreign sorceress of unknown origin had to be the real cause of any melodrama in Munchkinland. After all, it was well known throughout all of Oz that nothing of sizable importance ever occurred within such a tiny village. And as he watched his triumph get blown away, Ocknee, at last, knew this to be true.

ROCKING

Heidi Larsen

There's a leaf outside my window.
I've sat here for a while watching it
Flutter in the autumn wind.
A change has taken place,
It is no longer colorful.
It has defriended its youth,
Dry and brittle,
Change is on the horizon.
Winter will come, rustling will stop.
I watch for the sudden gust
That will separate leaf from its tree
Adding the leaf with its carpet of friends below.
It holds on strong, afraid to let go.
Each new gust comes, changing, stirring.
Cold winds prevail,
Dipping the leaf down to its depths,
Followed by high flight,
On wings of pleasure.
Up or down
It's always rocking,
Never still; carefree, wandering, unsettled,
Loosening its grasp on the branch.
A ship tossed at sea,
Storms that never still,
Its journey has begun.

I HEARD THE WIND WHISPER MY NAME

LuAnn Thibodeau

Feeling so lonely as I lie in bed,
With memories of you filling my head.
I heard the wind whisper my name,
I looked up and realized it was from Heaven that this whisper came.

The whisper continued, as it did say,
"I am still with you, 24 hours a day;
And even though we are physically apart,
I am always there, inside your heart.

I loved you so long and I love you still,
My passing was part of God's perfect will.
I am no longer suffering or in pain.
I am tending the gardens once again.

So when you find a penny, a feather, or butterfly,
Those are signs from me, because I want you to try
To return to the life that you love,
It warms and fits you, just like a glove.

Now, cry when you feel that you must,
But never lose faith, never lose trust.
Someday in Heaven with me you will be,
Where we'll be together for eternity.

Until then, my dear, I will dry,
Each and every tear that falls from your eye.
My love showers you from Heaven above,
Like sweet rain drops on the wings of a dove.

And when you feel sorrow, listen closely, I'll whisper in your ear.
Anytime you need me, I'll always be near,
Sending you hugs and kisses and love,
Coming from me in Heaven above."

THE POEM IN THE PARK

John Grey

I put the parchment down
on the bench for a moment
and suddenly the wind grabs it.

Seas have icebergs, birds have wings,
and all I got was this lousy
hand-written poem
fleeing down the breezy street
ahead of me.

A woman struts by me.
Her perfume engulfs my lungs.
My poem goes one way,
its fleshier self, another,
her scent beckoning me
to give up
one romantic pursuit for the other.

But instead I go on.
Oh please don't let if fly off
into the river.
I can see it now...
my splash versus words' ripples.

I catch up with opus 427
as it slaps against an oak trunk.
It was a poem about that tree
until the wind reminded me
such trees were once a nut like you.

AS THE WIND BLOWS

Edward Ahern

Caspar Volodka was a wind forecaster. Not a weatherman, but a high-paid consultant who predicted severe wind events. His uncanny ability to foretell these disasters saved his clients hundreds of millions of dollars.

He'd created the world's best model for the causes and effects of wind, but knew all too well how much he couldn't predict. It galled him, like sitting through a play while only knowing half the words.

Yolanda, his efficient number two, approached him one morning in their Boston office. In addition to running a staff of twelve she developed prospects, set pricing, oversaw accounting, and kept Caspar from annoying his customers.

"I have a prospect you need to make time for. He wants to offer you help."

Caspar had interrelated server-driven programs running on three adjacent monitors, and barely took the time to look up and smile. "Did you tell him I don't know enough to need it?"

"He's heard of your engaging personality. It's a Mr. McEnlil. He wants to discuss a business proposal with you, and needs an hour of your time. He's willing to pay double our initial consulting fee up front."

"Clearly has no head for business."

Yolanda smiled back at him. "Humor me. Be nice, don't hint that you think he's stupid, and we'll pocket enough to buy you another month of whatever it is you're noodling on."

"Yes dear. How soon will I need to be amiable?"

"You've just had a postponement, so next Wednesday, 10 am."

* * *

When Yolanda ushered in Mr. McEnlil her eyes were wide. Caspar snuck her a quizzical glance, but she just shook her head from side to side. And then Caspar understood why. McEnlil filled the room. Not physically, he was a middle-aged man of average height and girth. But his presence pushed all the stale air out the vents and replaced it with his personal ozone. Caspar suspected that McEnlil could convince him to sell his children.

"Mr. McEnlil, I'm not given to compliments, but you have a stage presence Beyonce would envy."

McEnlil smiled slightly. "Thank you, but I hope you're not too starstruck to listen to my proposal."

Yolanda hadn't left, and Caspar nodded for her to stay.

Caspar began. "Mr. McEnlil, ah, may I call you by your first name? It's not on your card."

"I don't use a Christian name, so just call me Enlil."

"Okay. Enlil, how can I help you?"

"It's how I can help you, Caspar. Your modeling for winds is elegant but, as you must know, unable to foretell many major weather events. I am the creator of a, let's say, different model and would like to provide you with guidance on an ongoing basis."

Caspar felt less awestruck. Enlil after all was just a door-to-door salesman with a great persona. "Thank you, Enlil but our model, even if flawed, is proprietary, and we couldn't bring in another system without weakening the fiduciary trust our customers have in us."

Enlil smiled broadly and Caspar felt like a hot desert wind was blowing over him. "It's so refreshing to hear corporate doublespeak again. What I'm suggesting would have no contact with or impact on your model. I would provide you with independent predictors of the same circumstances you're studying. I would do this at no cost to you until you are satisfied with the rightness of what I tell you."

Caspar's grin was forced. "Enlil, I'm prevented from telling you what we're working on."

"The weather conditions are uncertain but obvious. Let me guess. You have to be looking at the typhoon risks in Malaysia and the Philippines. As you should. Within the coming week there will be a major storm that will flatten unprepared construction sites in both countries. This afternoon you'll receive a courier package with the conclusions of my forecast. Compare what I predict with the actual occurrence. Then please call me at the number on my card."

Caspar decided that Enlil was certifiable but low risk, and

after a bit of prospect-stroking small talk, he ushered Enlil out to the elevator. Yolanda had remained in his office.

She started to speak. "He's…"

"He certainly is. I was getting ready to change my sexual preferences. It'll probably amount to nothing, but when his package arrives this afternoon, please have it brought in to me."

* * *

The text of Enlil's report was in a script rather than block letters, which Caspar thought affected. But after reading through the text and charts, he changed his mind. The Cuneiform-like letters matched Enlil's writing style and the direness of the conclusion.

Enlil predicted that in five days both Manila and Kuala Lumpur would be struck by cyclone strength winds that could cause multiple deaths and would severely damage anything not well secured. After checking his own models and regional weather forecasts Caspar laughed. There were some unsettled conditions, but no way this could happen within the next two weeks. He tossed Enlil's report into the stack to be shredded and moved on to serious work.

An hour later, after his subconscious had had time to digest the warning, Caspar pulled the report back out of the shredder pile and reread it. Maybe, just maybe, he thought. He walked over to Yolanda's work area, folder in hand. She was holding a staff meeting in her conference room.

Casper caught her attention through the glass wall and raised a finger. She excused herself and stepped out to meet him. "Bad timing, Caspar, we're into something."

"Naturally. When you're finished, I need you to do something stupid for me."

"Again? What is it?"

"McEnlil is predicting a weather disaster in the South China Sea. It's impossible, but I think we need to warn our clients and the regional weather centers that we've received a low probability report. Suggest that they take reasonable precautions."

Yolanda frowned. "But you think the report is junk. We lose a lot of credibility by pushing some end-of-the-world warning. Not to mention revenue."

Caspar's face puckered. "I know, I know. But I have to take precautions the first time Chicken Little warns me."

He handed Yolanda the folder. "Please arrange a broadcast warning with low probability. No specifics except for the dates and areas of possible impact. I'll put on my ridicule bib."

"You'll need it. We're going to lose any chance we have to be pompous."

* * *

The day after the storm hit, Caspar was flooded with calls, emails and texts. Most expressed thanks, but, inevitably, a few carped that Caspar hadn't assigned the cyclone a higher probability. Caspar suspected that those bitter were also those who hadn't taken precautions. And he knew from experience that some of the complainers would grudgingly remain customers. After the communication tide ebbed, he called Enlil. There were a series of clicks, as if his call was being relayed through multiple pathways.

"Mr. McEnlil, your prediction was accurate. Incredibly so."

"Please, keep calling me Enlil. Perhaps you should just appreciate the results. If this were a fairy tale, I'd have to do this three times for you to believe in me. Might we accelerate the process?"

"Of course. What do you suggest?"

"Send me two or three of your major concerns– storm surge flooding, fire storm winds, the circulation of air pollution, whichever are most troubling to you. As my predictions prove true, pay me—let's call it a thirty percent tithe from your profits for each incident. There is no need for any other compensation. One condition, however."

Caspar's thoughts were churning, but he managed to reply. "Yes?"

"I don't trust banks. The payment must be in gold – ingots, coins, jewelry – the shape doesn't matter. But it must be the equivalent of the 24-karat price. Delivered to an address I'll provide."

Caspar felt like an observer in the noisy common room of an asylum. "That's, that's very irregular. For tax purposes we would need…"

Cold air seemed to sublime from his cell phone as Enlil replied. "Your internal requirements are your concern. I'm offering you solutions at no cost unless they prove out. Shall we proceed?"

Caspar's fingertips felt numb. He was joining the crazies in the common room. "I, ah, I, sure, please give me your email address and I'll send you one or two problem items. Let's see what you make of them."

"Excellent, Caspar. I think we're going to become truly close. But please make it a text to this phone number. We'll talk again after you see the results I provide."

* * *

Caspar remained dubious about Enlil, and decided on innocuous tasking—the Sunday winds for a balloon race in France and a football game in Chicago's Soldier Field. Neither event involved clients or was remotely life threatening. Right or wrong, Caspar decided to say thank you and goodbye to Enlil. Better, he thought, to remain in ignorance than to partner up with a lucky loon.

Enlil called him back shortly after the text was sent. His tone was cold and Caspar caught a whiff of rotting seaweed. "The trivialities you asked about suggest that you're abandoning our discussion."

The thought crossed Caspar's mind that, aside from bartenders, Enlil was the most intoxicating individual he'd ever met. "Enlil, I'm sorry, but I'm not comfortable with the arrangement you proposed. I'll return your payment as a fee for your predictions, right or wrong. But I can't pass along recommendations without any understanding of how you've arrived at them."

"So, we will need the fairy tale steps after all. Very well. Here they are. Tell the organizer of the balloon race to postpone it by a day or a week, because the air will be calm and all the balloons will be suspended like bright pimples around the park. And tell the Chicago Bears coach that shortly before half time the wind will shift around to the north and blow so strongly that the team on the south side of the field will be unable to pass for any distance. Keep the earnest money, it is of no use to me. Once these predictions prove true, please call me back."

Caspar rechecked his forecast models and confirmed that Enlil's predictions were absurd. He sat on them in secrecy until Sunday when the balloons were marooned and the Bears lost 41-10 because they couldn't throw the ball in the second half. He ran another analysis that told him the odds of both unlikely events happening on the same day were 33,765 to 1. Then he called Enlil back.

"Enlil, I have too many questions to be handled on a phone call. Could we meet again? I can come to your office if you prefer."

"Ah, like an acolyte to his temple. Of course, my dear one. Shall we say next Thursday at 11am? I believe you are free. I will text you the directions. And I must have your oath on that which you hold sacred, that our conversation will be held in confidence."

Feeling like a frat pledge, Caspar said, "I so swear."

As he hung up, Caspar thought he smelt sandalwood, but decided it must be leftover cleaning solution. Directions appeared almost immediately on his phone, to a location in the Berkshires.

* * *

Caspar left in his car that Thursday morning at 5am and drove for several hours. Despite all the turnings he felt like he was being pushed by a tailwind. Enlil's address was no office. It looked like a nuclear shelter built into a hillside. Enlil met him at the reinforced steel doors. He seemed somehow taller and more solid.

"Welcome. I hope to the first of many visits."

"Is this…?"

"A bomb shelter? Yes, it is. But before then the Pocumtuc referred to it as the cave of the air, because of all the shifting breezes that seemed to come from nowhere and return to nothing. It suits me. Please come in."

Caspar was led into a huge open cavern under the hill. There were recessed lights, but no computers or electrical equipment. They sat on two heavily carved, high-backed chairs with rattan seating that looked like they'd come from Henry VIII's palace. As Enlil smiled Caspar felt like warm salt air washed over him.

"Did you wonder about my name? Enlil was a Sumerian god of air and wind, storms and turmoil, but also wealth and power. More powerful, some say than all the other gods in the Sumerian pantheon. I am his namesake."

'I'm sorry, but until I met you, I'd never heard the name."

"It is no wonder. With the sacking of Nippur, his priests and followers were killed or dispersed. It is as if Enlil went into seclusion for millennia. But I would like to bring the focus back."

Caspar wondered if the steel door was locked against a quick exit. "How do I fit into this? I don't think I can be helpful."

"Ah, but you can. This is an age of science, of mistrust until facts are 'proven.' And you are the leading technical expert on wind, on the essence of Enlil. With my guidance you can become the irrefutable oracle of wind science. And receive answers to the questions and ignorance that so deeply trouble you."

Enlil stood up, took three quick steps and stood directly behind Caspar's chair. Then he gently placed his hands on Caspar's shoulders.

Caspar jolted. He felt like his insides were being scooped out, like he was a human flute, making indescribable, inaudible sounds with Enlil's shifting breaths. He was being played, not as a con, but as an atmospheric instrument. When Enlil removed his hands, Caspar was saddened, knowing there was so much more music he wanted to make.

"How? What?"

"I wish to make you my face to the world, explaining things in words they accept, and re-instilling a healthy fear of my wrath. There is no higher calling."

Enlil returned to his chair. Caspar was trembling, not in fear, but in awe of what had just happened to him. "This is impossible, delusional."

"Should I enter you again?"

"I couldn't handle it."

"Perhaps not right now. But you will quickly grow accustomed."

Caspar realized what Enlil had said. "You'd punish people for not bending to your will?"

"I'm returning to my proper status, Caspar. Those who deny me must suffer."

"I–I have to leave, to think."

"Of course. Please keep your thoughts to yourself, and call me when you've reached a decision. The forecasted rain storm will hold off until after your return home."

* * *

The next morning, Yolanda appeared in the office almost immediately after Caspar's first coffee. "Tell me," she commanded.

Caspar wanted to, needed to. Yolanda was his reality principle, but he hesitated. She wouldn't believe him. "Just the same pitch. He provides forecasts that we reimburse him for. I'm still thinking it over."

She studied him with suspicious caring. "You seem different, more effervescent. Did he give you something?"

"Nothing." He hesitated. "What Enlil is proposing would not

only change how we would do business, it would change me. And I'm not sure I could stand it."

Yolanda moved closer. "Is it illegal? Were you threatened?"

Caspar laughed ruefully. "No, no, but I have to decide about what I might become."

Yolanda put a hand on his desk. "If you're worried, just tell him to get lost. We can do nicely without him."

"Yeah, but I don't want to do without what he can give me. I'll let you know as soon as I've made up my mind."

Yolanda glanced outside Caspar's window on her way out. "There's some kind of stationary whirlwind just beyond the glass. I've never seen anything like it."

He winced. "I have."

Caspar took two more days. He could live well without the extra money, and wondered how Enlil would treat him once the honeymoon was over. But the chance to work with the winds as if he were riding them was irresistible. He called Enlil from his office.

"Hello Enlil, I've been thinking about your proposal. What sort of obligation would this put me under?"

Wafts of cinnamon seemed to drift up from his phone. "Hello, my dear Caspar. There is no contract, no bondage. But you'll find that my knowledge and power are quite addictive. Quite. As we progress you will become my face to the world, both smiling and stern."

Caspar sighed. He felt like he was a fish caught up in a water spout with no idea where he would be dropped. But oh, the view. "Why don't you just do this on your own, Enlil?"

"Ah. I prefer to remain behind a curtain. There are actions and sacrifices best left to mankind to perform."

He was in the eye of the hurricane and he knew the calm would turn to chaos. But Caspar also felt an urgent need. "Very well, Enlil, I accept. The gold you would receive would clean out the jewelry district on 47th street. Should I hold shares in gold funds for you so you can cash out in gold whenever you like?"

Enlil laughed. It vibrated through Caspar's cell phone so hard he almost dropped it. "This is why I need a hierophant. Done."

The air was pungent as Caspar pocketed his phone. Yolanda came in. "What a beautiful aroma, it's like a church, like frankincense and myrrh."

"Let's hope it's not a sacrificial altar."

SPIRITS OF THE WIND

Kathy Chencharik

They ruffle my hair and caress my face
with hands, I cannot see.
They lift me up when I'm feeling down
these spirits so wild and free.

They always start out in a whisper
speaking words I cannot hear.
Yet, I try to listen closely
for I know they must be near.

They slowly flip through my notebook
writing words with invisible ink.
If only I could read what they write
and, know what they truly think.

Soon, they pick up momentum
like a thousand souls unleashed,
whipping in all directions
of north, south, west and east.

Someday, I may join in their game
of unseen Kick the Can,
but for now, my spirit is stuck here
confined to the body of man.

Previously published:
Worcester Magazine Oct. 1996
Athol Daily News Nov. 23 1996
Worcester County.Com 5/10/2004

WINDS OF CHANGE

WINDFALL

Chele Pedersen Smith

"Chase them. They're getting away!"

"Grab 'em!"

"Hurry!"

"Catch as many as you can!"

"Go for the ground."

"Mom, jump higher!"

The shouts from the crowd psyched Claire's adrenaline. Her hands quivered as the papers fluttered past. The churning vortex made it impossible to catch just one, and the billows only blew them around. Frustrated, she was standing in the middle of a ticker tape tornado.

From inside the tank, Claire could hear the faint cheers of the audience spurring her on. Teen daughter Lela's advice managed to trickle into her ear. *Jump higher? I'm fifty-five!* Plus, she could barely stand upright against the squall. But she had to try.

"Well, here goes nothing," Claire muttered. "I did do aerobics back in the 80s though!" She squatted, then sprang up as high as her five-foot frame allowed. Her fingers fringed the edge of a *hundred-dollar Benjamin*!

Progress! If only she had a trampoline. But no matter. It was up to her to save the day, and their mortgage! With a determined, darting tongue, she leapt again, thinking of her childhood poodle's springing-height. Reaching, stretching into the blinding whiteout…she snagged a bill from the *Monsoon of Moola* as it teased, then another, and a few more.

Finally! But what am I supposed to do with these? Frantic, Claire glanced around the twirling tunnel, hair whipping in her face. Her fists were overflowing, and there were still two minutes on the clock.

"Stick'em in your shirt, Mom!"

"Fill your socks!"

"Stuff them anywhere!" the crowd yelled.

"Remember," crooned the host's velvety voice, "what you grab, you get to keep."

Trembling, Claire crammed the bucks into her bra. *Could she win enough to pay off her house?*

She lurched, leapt, and came down with two more bills.

"One minute left," boomed the automatic timer.

Dazzled by dollars and the ticking time limit, something savage clicked inside Claire. She crouched low, snapping up the swirling grounders. She soared, channeling her inner poodle and then, claws out — Cha-Ching! — she conjured up copious cheddar. Claire shoved the currency into her clothing at Mach speed, thankful for expanding sweatpants.

"Thirty seconds left!" The digital voice matched the flashing red numbers.

Last chance. Vaulting off her toes, she decided to pirouette and go with the flow.

Almost in slow motion, she felt like a ribbon dancer. Spinning graceful and swanlike, she plunked a flurry of cash from the air. High to low she spiraled as the countdown zapped to zero. The wind disappeared and she sank to the floor.

The glamorous assistant opened the booth. Claire pranced out, bulging with banknotes. She was on her way to wealth! Well, enough to rid some stress, anyway.

Rich, the host, joined his contestant on the stage. "Did she do a fantastic job or what?" he flourished, baiting the audience. "We'll find out in a few minutes. Sorry, Claire, but this is where it gets tricky," warned the smooth-voiced master of ceremonies. He summoned someone off-stage and two handymen carried in a privacy screen. Then his gorgeous sidekick, Phyla, sashayed up to the plump mom and gently led her behind the divider.

In her stuffed sweats, Claire felt like a sumo wrestler next to the tall assistant, who sparkled in an emerald evening gown.

"Now we will extract the winnings," Phyla advised, sweet as can be. "Exciting, right? I really hope you win the million dollars."

"Thanks! Me too," Claire squealed, shutting her eyes with a prayer. "But whatever I caught will help a lot."

"Time to see how much!" The sidekick held out a money bag, and for a second, Claire thought it might be a deal dangler, a tempting trade. Would she risk it all? But no, the bag was empty, waiting to hold her loot.

With a deep breath, Claire unloaded her hidings. When she

began emptying her sweatpants, she couldn't help but laugh. The legs were bursting like sausage casings.

Phyla giggled as the money bag expanded. "I haven't seen anyone grab this much before!"

As they tamped down the contents to make room, Claire was confident she seized at least a thousand smackeroos, enough to help with the next house payment. Once Claire was de-monetized, Phyla helped her get dressed for the big reveal.

As the women emerged from the divider, Rich took the money bag. Perspiring rivulets ran down Claire's forehead and she suddenly hoped he wasn't going to run away with it. How much could you trust a "moola tunnel" set up at the Whitney Field Mall, anyway?

Riffs of money songs and crisscrossing spotlights built up anticipation while the bills shuffled through an automatic counter. The crowd closed in, waiting for the tally. Claire's three kids and her mother hovered in the stage wings, bouncing on their toes while pressing fists to their mouths. Staring out at the masses wedged between JCPenney and the food court, Claire's heart swelled. This was fate. Just when she needed it, *her* name was chosen from the hundreds of slips in the tumbler.

"And now, Claire," Rich purred, putting his arm around her. "Are you ready to see your grand total?"

She closed her eyes and nodded.

There was an extended drum roll and then a crashing cymbal. A monetary number flashed on the screen as a confetti cannon popped and more musical riffs filled the air.

"What?" Claire's mouth fell open. "No way!"

"Congratulations! This is amazing. It's a record-setting amount!" Rich clapped, whooping it up for the audience to join in.

"I can't believe it!" sputtered Claire, almost glaring at the $209.00 as if it were an enemy.

"It's awesome and you earned it! That's the most anyone on our Massachusetts tour has ever won!" Rich handed Claire a check while a rainbow of paper scraps rained on her parade.

"Thank you so much!" Secretly crestfallen, she stared at the cashier's check, smiling out at the crowd. "This will come in handy." Then she whispered to Rich. "I truly *am* grateful, but I swore I snatched *a lot* more than that."

"Yeah, that's the thing," he comforted. "Most of the tank's bills are one-dollar wonders."

She braved a grin at their gimmick as the newspaper photographer snapped her photo. Rich's assistant ushered her to the back.

"It's not the jackpot but it truly is a lot," Phyla assured. "Most people only get five or ten bucks if they can catch any at all."

"Wow, guess I did have a lucky streak. Thank you!" The gals hugged. Phyla went off to her makeshift dressing room and Claire's family flocked around her.

"Way to go, Mom!" Lela cheered. "I didn't know you were so agile!"

"Oh, I hope it looked as elegant as it was in my head," Claire worried, "and not like a boulder doing ballet."

"It was surprisingly demure!" her mother, Mara, reassured.

Claire's younger sons tugged on her sleeves.

"Since we're rolling in dough now, can we get a pretzel each?" Michael snorted at his own joke.

"And slushies," Aaron added.

Claire laughed. "I think we have enough for a few."

While the kids climbed on interactive art and snacked, Claire confided in her mother.

"Instead of the windfall I thought I grabbed, I got the wind knocked out of me." She slurped a sad, loud gurgle of air through her straw. "I'm thankful, really, but I so wanted to save our house from foreclosure. I imagined an incredible surprise for Felix when he came home from his business trip. Then he wouldn't have to work so hard."

Mom patted her back. "I know, dear. It was worth a shot. Would've been a godsend but I'm kind of glad you didn't get the grand prize. Can you imagine all those vultures hounding you for money? At least the smaller amount helps with Lela's orthodontic payments."

"True," Claire sighed. "You'd think with our full-time jobs we'd never have money trouble."

Mara nodded in sympathy. "Well, kids are expensive and that electrical problem threw you off-kilter. Don't worry. It will all work out."

"It's always something." Claire blew out a breath. "Earlier this year, the paperboy broke a dormer window with his bad aim."

"But what a power arm," laughed Mara. "He should try out for the Red Sox."

Claire chuckled despite her glum mood. "Guess I'll call an agency for help on Monday." Sitting on what appeared to be an abstract fuchsia French bulldog, she shifted a few times. "Gee, these art blobs aren't built for comfort."

"That's for sure." Mara stood and stretched. "But they're vibrant enough to snap anyone out of a mall trance."

The kids ran over.

"Guess what?" Aaron gushed. "These cute animal benches are for sale! Can we get one? Please?" He fell to his knees, grasping his hands like a bouquet.

Michael caressed the shiny curve of an art piece. "It can be our pet and it doesn't need walks, or food, water, or newspapers!" he rambled.

Lela looked up from her phone. "Dad would like those selling points."

Claire shot Mara a disdained look. "What were you saying about vultures, Mother?"

***

It had been a long day of anticipation and let-downs. While Claire whipped up tacos and fiesta rice, the boys were still lobbying for a ceramic canine. Over dinner, she told the kids she'd think about getting a "Picasso" pet if they ate their broccoli. It was one of her time-stallers, like the stunts she pulled in stores. Somehow it always worked, hiding a coveted toy behind a less-popular plaything so it would be there for "next time, maybe."

Now that Michael and Aaron were snoozing in bed, and Lela was curled up streaming her favorite show (thanks to Mara's account), Claire was eager to shed her sweats. She made a cup of tea and changed into fluffy PJs, her laptop waiting on the bed to plot the next bill-shuffle strategy.

There, that was better! She scooped up the clothes heap and threw them in the hamper. Colorful scraps fluttered to the floor. *Ugh, damn confetti. No wonder it felt like a tag was bugging me all day.*

She vacuumed the area and then shook the clothing from the hamper to see if any other stragglers hitchhiked home. A piece of crumpled paper fell out of the tee shirt. *Oh, right. The Monsoon of Moola's rules and regulations, and all of that legalese.*

Straightening it out to read, she realized it wasn't paper. "Ooh, I won big, another dollar!" she giggled. But when she looked closer, she saw the "one" was followed by lots of zeros. "Can't be!" Her hands shook and she nearly dropped the cash, trying to hold it up to the light. *Was it real, or just a game show greenback?*

Claire ran to her desk. She fetched the special pen she used when she sold Mary Kay on the side at craft fairs. Swiping two marks on the bill's corner, she smiled when the amber ink remained. Not counterfeit! *Hmmm, had the money gotten lodged during the big sweep?* Well, her instinct was right. She *had* caught a caboodle more than what was revealed. She thought of Phyla's inspection and lingering hug. Was it an oversight, or a safe way of gifting it without the hoopla? However it happened, it was a feat of fate … a windfall, after all.

GRASSHOPPERS

Carlene Gadapee

When the wind takes on a corrective edge, I am caught
by endings, long after harvest, when leaves are brown
or gone, and the grass is brittle, frost-burnt and sagging
around the bases of shrubs and trees. I test gray weather

stripping, check for gaps, and seek out thermal curtains.
I must shut out the light now, or limit it to a few frugal
hours of milky-white when the sun seeps around clouds

and reaches hesitant fingers to caress bare striplings
of roses. The rattle of corn sheaves tied to lamp posts
sounds like dry rice in a metal basin. Do we have enough
to sustain ourselves, or should we count the grains?

CAN YOU SMELL IT?

Carlene Gadapee

Can you smell it? The air is amber, like honey,
leaves shimmer and shiver their way
through the humid breeze, sifting slowly to settle
on grass long dead and crisp. So much golden light
comes from distress. Droughts push trees to shed
leaves, precious jewels discarded and scattered,
whispering onto surfaces. But there are warnings:
wood smoke, skittering chipmunks, ghost-cries
of migrating Canada geese performing aerobatics,
floating and turbulent, arcing through haze.
Hints of cooler days filter in the shadows. I am alert
to changes, hushed hedges, to crickets singing sleep.

FIREFLY WINDS

Heidi Larsen

Circles of petticoats that danced in the breeze,
Thick golden locks that bounced as she sneezed,
Chasing zephyrs that pulled her along,
Barefoot and giggling, she skipped to a song.

A song meant for Daddy with a secret delight,
She had learned it herself, to sing it that night.
The child's warm toes slipped over the grass,
Waiting for Daddy to come home to his lass.

Intense moonbeams cast down their spell,
And the Canterbury-clothed child resembled an angel.
A vision of white seemed to float to the tree,
Where her wide, hopeful eyes did struggle to see.

She saw someone; she was unsure quite who.
If it wasn't him, what would she do?
At last, she sighed; there was nothing to fear,
He had made it; he was finally here.

The young child laughed with sparkles in her eyes,
As she ran to her Daddy to give her surprise.
A faint smile grew o'er his dark wrinkled face
When he saw his child bubbling over with grace.

Tis child and father hand in hand
Walking together upon their land.
Firefly winds carried them along.
The magic of a child, the magic of a song.

METAMORPHOSIS

(a prose poem)

Kathy Bennett

One last hoorah of Indian solstice beckoned me to play, running and skipping like a child on the vacant acreage where my ancestors' homestead once graced. To visit my roots, a nostalgic thing indeed, but to revert to my childhood, such an odd thing to do.

I drink up the sunshine and relished the crisp air. I frolic in the meadow of tall grass all mellow and yellowed. Just beyond the grove, I can't resist rolling in loosened leaves gliding downward one by one from majestic maples and ornery oaks onto the kaleidoscope carpet below.

And there I lay for some time, in wanton abandon, as the tepid air caresses and coaxes my body into blissful slumber . . .

Flapping flocks of migrant blackbirds call overhead.

My eyelids flutter in the waning daylight. I seem to glide upward onto my feet and all the while Mother Earth's breath billows my auburn tresses. My entire five-foot, three-inch frame feels willowy and light as the breeze itself, and I think to myself that perhaps all the breathless revelry expended earlier shed some idle weight around my middle, whereupon I look, and then I *gasp* in disbelief!

Unable to move, I stand utterly stunned, only to find that my feet are planted firmly in the soil! My legs and torso now a green, leafy stem mildly swaying.

Swaying is my mind in twilight time. I raise up my heavy helianthus head to look up to the heavens, my inflorescent face searching for impossible, but infinite, *plausibilities.*

Airy autumnal ribbons, unfurling and unending, rustle in my ears.

My hands are no longer hands. They are leaves, and they rustle in the wind.

My wisps of hair are no longer hair. They are brilliant yellow petals and they, too, ruffle. A smattering of my buttery petals release into the air and away they go. They go with all other shed foliage that has been loosened since the beginning of time, to mulch and to fertilize the same ground I once tread upon with two human feet.

I've become a sunflower.

Have I actually progressed from self-destructive human qualities to this sort of splendid simplicity in which my natural purpose and God-given attribute is to beautify the landscape? Or to uplift? Or to nourish with my essence?

The sun sinks. And so does my spirit. I bow my helianthus head to meditate.

The cool night air bids me dormancy. However, in the morning I may wonder "is this a blessing or is it a curse?" Ah, but it is not for me to question the one and only Almighty Creator. I simply hope to make my mark on this good earth, and when I awaken with dawn's first rays, will I proudly stand up tall to all the inhumanity of this life by showing the world the Way to Heaven?

Or will I be apathetic like most of mankind who trample hope underfoot and wallow in their insatiable void? God forbid I be forever stuck in budding metamorphosis – feet firm on the ground, *yet always looking for something – someone – beyond my own space.*

Interconnectedness. It defies singular space. Yet wild creatures all thrive within the laws of nature: sun, rain, air, changing seasons and the telling of gentle breezes.

Amazing how even by instinct there seems to be a peaceful coexistence among varied species who rely on their eyes and other senses. All have purpose. All are connected and are working within the expanse of creation. They all follow law, hierarchy. Together, they are beautiful.

Questions collecting dust in forgotten recesses along the labyrinth of my life billow across my mind, waiting for light in this willowy metamorphosis.

Christ-light and Spirit-wind are always there. In the atmosphere or on the horizon. World turns, and these are always here. O my soul – epiphanous – in the gentlest puffs of hope and the sighs of conviction in its quiet subtlety!

On the 'morrow when I awake, as surely as I dig down into my roots, may I take in my fill of light – glorious light – emanating from the rays of heaven.

Otherwise, I would simply be crouched down in shame or

lost in ambiguity if I just remain as one whose soul and spirit mimics the elusive autumn wind.

Nicole Lachance

A CHILD'S DREAMS

Lorri Ventura

In her dreams she drives an ice cream truck
And hands free fudgesicles to all the children.
She cures cancer
Ends wars
Reverses climate change
And speaks all languages fluently.
She spreads kernels of beauty and hope
Wherever she goes
The way Miss Rumphius blanketed the earth
With lupine seeds.
Best of all
She lives in a house full of cats
That purr her to sleep at night
So that she can save the world

LITTLE PINK FLOWER

Molly Chambers

Little pink flower
floats above the clear vase.
What happened to you?
Where is your green stem?
You never grew
to reach the sky.
Only your long, white roots
reach into the deep, clear water.
Now your struggle seems
almost over.
We all strive
to reach that high goal.
But somehow
you never made it.
Only your sudden, sweet flowering
gave a brief perfume
to our winter kitchen.
You looked out the window
over the snow cloaked grasses.
Cold winds snuck through the window crack.
You shivered in the cold
longing for a spring
you will never know.

SPRING, A SEASON FOR DREAMING

Mary J. Kellar

Spring is a season for dreaming
Things coming in days ahead
Flowers blooming in splendid beauty
As they sprout up from garden beds

There will be dreams of beach days
Of walks neath the stars late at night
And wonderful rides in the country
As the whole world turns green and bright

Dreams of fires on sandy beaches
Roasting hot dogs and marshmallows too
Springtime's an excellent time for dreaming
Of all the grand things you will do.

A DAUGHTER OF THE REVOLUTION

R. S. Fox

I mean really it's funny, horribly so: the nakedness of her fraud. She sits by the bank, with the blankets and the coin-rattle-cup and all that, with a cardboard sign that says "HOMELESS AND PREGNANT PLEASE HELP," about as thin as I am. The eyes, no redder than mine, are mopped with an utterly dry tissue, in the way nobody does when actually crying. This woman is probably homeless. She's probably not pregnant, and definitely not crying.

But she probably does need help.

I'm in Boston, deepest Nova Anglia, land of Polar and Utz and non-rhotic Rs and the mighty slave-raping forefathers of the liberal democratic empire rotting in black boxes under the cobbles. The beggars are many; there are fewer than at home, I note, or at least fewer in plain view. Probably there are more, actually, but the cops have a way of beating you so you'd rather slink into the alley and freeze-starve-rot than risk another beating by begging on the street. Poverty cannot be abolished, not in this time and place, but it can be terrified into never showing its face, so the young Sons of Liberty never question their superiority to those *other* countries, the ones where the poor show their faces without fear of rebuke and thus cannot be rendered ontologically dubious. C'est la vie.

As I stoop to give the requisite pittance I cannot find it in my heart, as I suspect my traveling companions do, to fault her even one iota for her deception. Truth is a luxury I can afford.

How easy it is to spurn God when one never once has needed a hateful father to hide beneath before plague, before the coming Hunnic flood, before the wrath of the Lord Paramount, before famine, cholera, rape, the dark and unknowable sky…

Not all can afford to face the world and know that they believe and state what they think and know to be true. To lie is to survive in conditions in which one ought to die. And who amongst us would not survive given the chance?

This is what I am thinking as I allow myself to pretend I have been duped. I will tell you what I think she is thinking:

Dumb fucking tourist rube has apparently never seen an actual crying person in his goddamn fucking life but hey, his loss is my gain.

All Rs therein are of course non-rhotic.

This, mind, might be my own bigotry, that this is what I think she thinks. I think I'm probably right, though.

I continue on my way along the Freedom Trail, and she stays exactly where she is. Of the three beggars I gave alms to only she was a liar. Maybe this weakens my defense of her. Or maybe the others were the real frauds, for they, unlike her, were not so desperate as to need to lie.

Here is the steeple of the Episcopal church from which that sainted silversmith called down that the British were coming, only he didn't, and in fact most probably would say if asked that he *was* British. Fledgling nations are always desperate enough, at first, to lie about the circumstances of their birth to make it a myth worth telling, a light by which to live. Next to it is what was the chapel of the Waldensians, that sect of self-conscious erstwhile Catholics so very protective of their modesty. One can imagine how the Anglo-Catholic pomposity of Revere's own temple, the looming threat of its hypodermic steeple, weighed upon the poverty-sworn souls of Waldo's faithful.

The Waldensians all died. The Episcopal church bought their chapel, and now it is a gift shop. C'est la vie.

DISCONSOLATE

Karen E. Wagner

It's the sky, this pink gray sky
rides high with rumbles afar.

Dark in nature, long fingers stretch
earthward, spread a serrated air.

Low clouds cut my vision short.
I feel the might of an oncoming storm.

Treed leaves rip upward and off.
I'm whipped raw. Even if it doesn't pour

and then it does. That first drop hits me square.
Unexpected torrents try to sweep my feet.

Streams hurtle. Ponds burst their misted walls
flush bogs, wetland plants succumb to rushed waters.

Fierce winds uproot tall pines. Crush hay fields.
I stagger, fall flat like a rotted tree.

Nature shows her prowess again. I'm tiny
in her presence. My plans are even smaller.

Jagged streaks of fire in the darkest quadrant
precede the bang of pagan thunder.

Earth exhales her intemperate breath.

THE WIND IS MY ANXIETY

Mackenzie Scanlon

The wind is my anxiety
I can't see but I can feel it take over me.
I'm a piece of paper that gets lost in mid-air
through a gust of intense worry.
I'm told to ride it out and let the rush of the wind
help me become who I was made to be.
But I'm only half of a story
with an ending that I can't yet see.
The chill leaves me restless
with racing thoughts and endless ideas.
I am words about to be spoken
without even knowing any of the criteria.
I panic about the landing and if I'll make it
dead or alive.
But I know I can't avoid my destiny
I'm meant to leave the past behind.

ROCKS

Tom Anthony

I

The sun does wonders for ledge
revealing the soft heart of granite,
baring marble's soul
to the shared ancestry
of glacial gravel.

Gravel – crushing and chipping,
washing and polishing
molds us all,
for a purpose to be served.

We pass judgment every day
before we perish and
stone gets the last word
repeating the epitaph,
when time washes it away.

II

Crawling out on a heated,
pillowed massif, the old man
mumbles to himself
of what lies within.
He says he's seen it all.

Perhaps it is the weight,
perhaps it is the time of day
but rocks left heaped upon each other
always find a way
to tumble down together.

Hardly anyone volunteers, it's up to me.
The soft ones first,
then the characters,
then those that interfere,
and those well, because they're here.

Those that haven't far to go—
down where the big guys,
Shoulder-to-shoulder
Burrow in their beds and grumble
"Not me, no way, no how."

III

We've been there; we've been a wall.
We've danced across the water
and caused the surf to roar.
We've done our share of mischief –
we've been potatoes,
and a damned effective shore.

So, here we go again.
Every generation takes its turn
and diminishes us with effort.
What was good ten years ago
no longer seems to matter.
We find our way back
and become someone else's purpose.

We'll be back; we'll be back.
I can't say when, but I know it.
I already see the plan
even if I do not know the woman
or the man with roughened hands
who will pry us loose
for another bout
of keeping someone in or out.

5.97

THE RIVER ON UNCLE JOE'S FARM: THE SUMMER I GREW UP

Benjamin Fine

Uncle Joe, my mother's older brother, was a cantankerous man. Tall, bald, and muscular, he chewed a cigar and muttered when he spoke. One-third of his vocabulary consisted of the single word goddamn.

He lived on the farm where he and my mother had grown up. It was a truck and vegetable farm when they were children, and their parents barely eked out a living. After they died, Uncle Joe changed it into a tree farm. He supplied landscape trees to most of the local nurseries around the small upstate New York town, Munstern. His Appalachian hillbilly lifestyle did not reflect his success. Nevertheless, my mother once told me in confidence he was one of the wealthiest men in Munstern and admitted that he had helped her out when needed.

My mother had married at 20 and moved further south to Ulster County in the Catskill Mountains, where I grew up. We visited Uncle Joe at least once a year, and he and my mother, as different as night and day, seemed to get along. I found Uncle's Joe bluster annoying, and I was uncomfortable sleeping at his farm. The rooms we slept in when we visited were filthy. I hated to step foot in his bathtub. We filled a pan from the sink and poured it into the bowl to flush the broken toilet. The kitchen had days-old dishes piled in his sink, the pans caked in grease.

On the other hand, my mother was picky and kept our house in Ulster sparkling clean. So that was how I expected a home to be. The old farmhouse he and Mom had grown up in, which looked like a nice place with a big wrap-around deck, was kept empty. Uncle Joe lived in a small shack that he built nearby. He never explained why.

When I was little, I snuck into the old house just to see it. The old furniture, and I told my friends back in Ulster that I had been in a haunted house. I half expected the pictures on the wall to have moving eyes like in the movies. Both my mom and Uncle Joe had their own rooms that seemed to me to be big and comfortable even though their parents were quite poor.

Uncle Joe never married and seemed to be the ultimate loner except for the local woman Winnie that he kept company with. She was a legal secretary in Munstern, although a bit strange. Her job required intelligence, and I heard that Winnie was competent at her job, but she seemed to me to be kind of slow. She wore old dresses with lace collars and big flowing skirts and would have fit nicely with Judy Garland in *Meet Me in St Louis*. Winnie lived with her mother, Mrs. Stone. She had bluish-white hair that made her look ancient, and she acted a bit batty, carrying an umbrella, rain or shine. However, Winnie and Uncle Joe seemed to get along well, and he often went out with her.

Despite the fact that I hated going there when I was seventeen and about to enter my junior year in high school, it was on Uncle Joe's farm that I grew up.

I played football for the Ulster Ravens, my high school team. I was a middle-sized linebacker and also boxed as a light heavyweight for the local Y. Coach Damendorf from the Ravens had arranged summer jobs for the team working at a nearby mountain resort. We were to work as the grounds crew at the hotel, a borscht belt getaway place for New York City before travel became so cheap. Coach Damendorf ran a summer camp attached to the resort, and the team would live on the property. In the late afternoons, Coach held football practice for the team on the hotel grounds. Past teams loved the arrangement, and I was excited about going. However, my mother's husband, that scumbag drunk, Lew, told my mother that I wasn't mature enough to go.

"He'll just get in trouble, Sue. You know him." Lew's word was final, and I was then stuck for the summer at home.

I had worked for my Grandpa Ed in his roofing business for the previous three summers. Ed was my father's father and the one tie I still had to my dad, who died when I was six. I idolized Grandpa Ed and loved working for him even though it was heavy work, and he didn't take it easy on me. I was his gofer, carrying material up and down the ladder while Grandpa worked on the roof. He also told story after story and treated me like an adult. Sadly Grandpa had died the previous November, crushing the only good part of my family world and leaving me no filter for Lew's insults and beatings.

I looked around my town, and although I knew almost all the

shop owners I couldn't find a summer job. So then, one evening sitting at the dinner table, I joked to Lew and my mom, "Well, I guess I'll have to sponge off of you guys this summer." Lew jumped up, grabbed me by the collar, and slapped me hard across my face. My sister Annie started to cry, but I kept it in. I wouldn't show that he got to me.

"You worthless, lazy shit," Lew yelled. "You're not sponging off us. If you can't find another job, you'll come to work for me. I could use you. I won't be as easy on you as your Grandfather. You'll work your tail off."

Why my mother, a tough, competent woman who worked for a reputable real estate company, allowed him to bully us like that, I don't know. I've never figured out my mother's personality with Lew. Her life with him was nothing like what she projected to the rest of the world. I didn't like Uncle Joe, but he was protective of my mom, and I'm certain he would have killed Lew if she ever let on how he treated her.

Lew was a building contractor and had a decent business. I often did part-time work for him, but he was drunk most of the time and treated me and the other workers like garbage. The last thing I wanted was to spend a whole summer with him.

Two days after that slap, my mother told me, "I called my brother, and you're going up there to work on his farm for the summer. I think it would be better for you than working for Lew."

As much as I disliked Uncle Joe, I knew she was right. In her own way, my mom had done what she could.

When school let out in June, my mom drove me and my bags up to Munstern. I remembered it well. Joe's shack and main house sat off of a two lane state route right next to a small river. The road from the farm to the center of Munstern crossed the river on a high bridge that replaced a smaller bridge that used to wash out each spring. The road to the old bridge was still there, but the lower bridge was gone.

When I was younger and we visited, my mom and I often sat by that river, and she told me where she, Joe, and their cousins would play as children. I would throw stones into the river and try to reach the other side while she told me stories of her childhood.

Uncle Joe had ten seasonal employees who lived in a bunkhouse near his main shack. "It will be good for him to live in the bunkhouse house with the workers, Sue," Joe told my mom. I preferred living in the bunkhouse since his shack was so filthy.

The seasonal workers were a rough bunch. Most of them had other jobs during the winter. We slept dormitory-style in the bunkhouse and ate our meals in an attached communal kitchen prepared by full-time cooks. I quickly learned there were two acknowledged leaders among the workers, and most decisions went through them. They had their own private rooms in the bunkhouse.

Mike Boritz, the head honcho, drove a big Harley and looked like a rebel biker. The local bikers steered clear of him, sort of a lone hero. He was big, blonde, and massively built, at least six foot three or four and two hundred forty pounds. He could have been a professional wrestler. My arms were big and cut from boxing and football, but they looked puny next to Mike's. I never saw him fight, but it was clear that none of the workers or locals would stand up to him. He had a girlfriend in town, Stacy, blonde and pretty and built as well as Mike but in a girl way. She also had the biggest blue eyes I have ever seen. Even though they might fear Mike, other men couldn't help but stare at Stacy.

Mike's best friend was another big biker. Walt Savage didn't work for Uncle Joe but visited quite often. He worked for an excavation company and was always asking Mike to come to work with him. Walt and Uncle Joe seemed to be on good terms, and when Walt visited Uncle Joe would talk to him in his annoying bluster.

Ron Reddway was Mike's second in command, although Ronnie usually acted independently. He was in his twenties like Mike but much smaller, about my size, with dark olive skin and a hawk nose. Ron's mother was Lebanese, and his father a local Yankee, Clyde Reddway, whom all the workers seemed to know. Ronnie always looked like he was up to something. He drove a souped-up Cadillac Seville with a truck engine that made that Caddy fly. On their Harleys and Ronnie in his Cadillac, Mike and Walt made quite a fearsome trio on the roads. The local biker Hell's Angels gang even moved aside if they saw them coming. Ronnie had a girlfriend in town, Barbara, who happened to be the wife of a local pharmacist. Ronnie was popular with the workers since he ran a baseball pool and seemed to have an endless supply of dope.

The work on Uncle Joe's farm was heavy but not hard, and I enjoyed it. It was easier than the roofing work I had done for Grandpa Ed. We moved trees and loaded supplies, peat moss, and such, from train box cars. We also watered and trimmed the trees and delivered them. Ronnie and Mike would do the planting. Uncle Joe yelled his commands, although Ronnie and Mike knew what they were doing.

The workers sat around in the evenings, drinking and smoking dope. The talk was local gossip about girls, parties, and fights. The guys were all at least in their twenties, two were married with wives in other towns, but they acted as if they were still in high school. I fell easily into their conversations as I had with my friends back home. However, it wasn't until the fight one evening that I stopped being Uncle Joe's nephew and became just one of the guys.

Tommy Smith was a nasty Irish kid who disliked me for some reason. He drank too much and had Celtic skin with blood vessels covering his face. When I sat with the workers in the evening, Smith grumbled about letting Joe's kid hang out with them.

"Don't say anything," Tommy warned the others, "the kid will rat us out to his Uncle."

I kept my mouth shut. I didn't want to make enemies. That evening I had a beer in my hand, and for some reason, Tommy Smith asked me for it. I told him, "No. Go get your own." He said, "You're a cheap Jew bastard like your uncle."

I took stuff like that at home from Lew, but I wasn't going to take it from Tommy Smith. "You'd better apologize, you prick," I said, standing over him.

He had a piece of wood in his hand, swung it, and hit me over the head. I should have fallen, but I just shook it off and kept coming at him. Seeing me, Tommy panicked. I hit him three times in the face, opening a gash in his veiny skin each time. His face seemed to explode, and blood spurted out. With his face and shirt covered in blood, I went to hit him a fourth time, but the other guys grabbed me. Tommy Smith slinked off to clean himself up. Mattie Barone, one of the workers, said. "Wow, kid, you're tough like your uncle." He turned to the group and said. "This kid's all right. He can hang with us."

From that point on, I was just one of the guys. Mike and Ronnie sort of adopted me. On some evenings, I'd ride in Ronnie's Cadillac the four miles to Munstern center, and we'd chill out at the Nest, the local tavern. We'd drink and shoot pool, and I was never carded – it made me feel like a grownup.

I met most of the other townies there, including Mike's girlfriend and Ronnie's married lady friend Barbara. She was heavy with big soft bosoms. She'd hug and kiss me on the cheek, press her chest against me, and say, "What a cute kid," and laugh. She always gave me the vibe that I could have her if I wanted, and I didn't think Ronnie would mind, but I never tried anything.

Some afternoons they would give me some time off. "Let the kid rest a bit," Mike would say, and I'd have a couple of hours to myself. I often walked down to the river and sat where the lower bridge used to stand. The road still went toward where the lower bridge used to be. I'd sit there and throw rocks into the river. Just like I did as a kid, I'd try to reach the far bank. I'd think about the times before my father died. Maybe memory is different than reality, but in my memory we had such a happy home, always laughing and doing family stuff.

My Dad was a roofer like my Grandpa Ed. One day without warning, he had a heart attack and slipped off the roof. He was dead when he hit the ground. It was hard on all of us. My mother grieved for a year.

A friend set her up with Lew. He was tall and thin and made a good first impression. My mom married him, but he turned out to be a drunk and fucked my life up. He started beating me almost immediately over every little thing. My mother said nothing; she looked away and let it happen. He liked to be in complete control, and I saw him slap her several times. He acted nice to my sister Annie who never talked back to him. For the past two years I knew I could kick his ass, but I never built up the courage to beat the shit out of him. Finally, sitting by that river, all of this became crystal clear to me, and I decided that when I returned home I wouldn't take it anymore.

Ronnie threw big parties in the bunkhouse on some weekends, and Uncle Joe looked the other way. They put a keg out front, and the place swam in beer, weed, and local women. Because of the fight I wasn't introduced as Joe's teenage nephew anymore, just one of the workers. That's how I met Cindy.

Cindy Lavoy was a cute redhead with curly hair and big brown eyes. She had freckles and a gorgeous body. When I first met her, Cindy wore short shorts that hugged her behind and a tank top that left little to the imagination. She was only twenty but already married to a state trooper. They lived about thirty miles away. She drove a hot white Mustang convertible and came to the parties in Munstern for the dope and to screw around.

Ronnie introduced us. "Cindy, this is the new guy Danny. I think you'll like him." It was easy to make her laugh, and then we made out with her in her car. After that, she adopted me, and we'd ride in that white Mustang all over. With her, I learned the pleasures of cheap motels and how much more comfortable they are than cramped back seats. Back home, I had done stuff with girls, but I was still a virgin when I started going with Cindy. That changed in a hurry. The other guys were jealous because everyone wanted Cindy. Ronnie told me that I was lucky because she usually liked older men. She had even been with my Uncle Joe. I don't know whether I thought less of Uncle Joe because he was cheating on his girlfriend Winnie or thought more of him because he was actually human. When Uncle Joe found out I was hanging around with Cindy, he winked at me and said, "Good Goddamn going Kid."

Ronnie told me to get Cindy one weekend, and we would go with his married girlfriend Barbara, swimming and picnicking at a nice lake about a hundred miles away. Cindy left her white Mustang at the farm. Mike and his girlfriend came on his Harley. Mike rode the windy back road next to Ronnie's Caddie and we made it to the lake in just over an hour, averaging well over eighty on that narrow two-lane route. Barbara had made fried chicken, and we swam and drank beer. Then, in the late afternoon, I lay with Cindy on a blanket and made out. It felt good to have Cindy with me and that the guys treated me as an adult.

On a few evenings, I accompanied Ronnie on his drug runs. He drove to a lakefront park near Uncle Joe's farm to meet people and sell weed. One night two kids accused him of cheating them. I looked on in awe as Ronnie beat up one of the kids, who was a great deal bigger than him. The other kid, a big football lineman type, started to come at me, but he backed off when I threw a punch that landed on his face and drove him backward. Ronnie thanked me for standing by his side.

Some bad news came from that same lake a few weeks after that. Walt Savage and his Harley were found in the water. He must have been going too fast and couldn't make one of the turns. Mike told me that the speedometer on his bike stuck at 95 mph, and the police told him Walt had flown fifty feet in the air before he hit the lake. Mike and Walt were good friends, but Mike acted as if it were nothing. Accidents could happen, and often did, seemed to be his attitude. I think because I lost my father so early and was heartbroken when I lost Grandpa Ed, I took Walt's death harder than Mike's. I went with Mike, Ronnie, and Uncle Joe to the funeral at St. Ambrose, a local Catholic Church, and sat quietly during the mass.

I was at the farm for a full eight weeks, and September was approaching quickly. I was having the time of my life and wanted it to continue, but my mom called and told me she was picking me up the following Saturday. When she arrived, Mike, Ronnie, and Uncle Joe were there to say goodbye. I placed my bags in her car and turned to look at Mike's big Harley. I had never been on it. "Take me for one ride, Mike?" I asked.

He shook his head. "You sure?" he asked. "If you've never been, it might be scary."

"No, I'm certain, Mike," I told him. "Just one ride." I climbed onto the back, and he sped towards Munstern center. We rode without helmets, and as he picked up speed, it all seemed out of control, like we were just a razor's width from death. Suddenly, as we approached the fork by the bridge, he turned right to the lower bridge that wasn't there. I don't know if I yelled, but he laughed. He lifted the front tire as we got close to the river bank, and we flew over the stream. While in the air, I tipped my head back and felt really alive for the first time. He touched down seamlessly on the far bank and continued riding as if it were nothing. When we got to Munstern center, he drove by the Nest, and then we turned around and headed back to the farm.

After saying final goodbyes and driving south, my mom asked, "It must have been tough with Uncle Joe, but I'll bet it was better than working for Lew."

"It was all right," I told her. Then, thinking of Cindy, I said. "I'd like to come back and work here next summer."

"Well, things are a bit different now," my mother told me. "Lew and I split up, so you don't have to deal with that anymore."

My life changed for the better with that sentence. I had resolved to fight back when he started with me, but now I didn't have to.

During my junior year, I met Angela, who became my regular girlfriend. It was nothing like with Cindy, typical teenage stuff.

Although one time she did tell me that I seemed so much more experienced than any other guys she had gone out with. Her father owned a trucking company in town, so the following summer in my senior year, I didn't go back to Uncle Joe but worked driving a truck for Angela's father. My mother had bought me a car, and I drove up to the farm one weekend to visit. Mike and Ronnie weren't working there anymore. They had started their own construction company, and a whole new crew was in the bunkhouse. Uncle Joe spoke with me almost civilly.

"I heard Ronnie," Uncle Joe told me, "is some sort of big gangster here in town; drugs and gambling. I always liked him, though. He married that druggist's ex-wife." Uncle Joe had also broken up with Winnie and had a new prettier girlfriend, Lanny. At least he's human.

During my senior year, with Angela as my girlfriend and my experience on the farm, I walked with a swagger. I felt like a man, and I really believe that I grew up that summer on Uncle Joe's farm.

OUR CONTRIBUTORS

ABOUT OUR PRESIDENT

Steven Michaels is the author of *Sweet Life of Mystery*, a parody of the whodunit genre. He has been featured on The Satirist website for his scintillating take on current affairs, and has written, produced, and directed over twenty plays for students at Winchester School in New Hampshire. Steve founded the Quabbin Quills in 2017 and was instrumental in creating the first anthology, *Time's Reservoir* and he hopes you have enjoyed the work he has featured in all of Quabbin Quills' anthologies. He is also very thankful to all the authors who have come to share his writer's dream.

ABOUT OUR PUBLISHER

Garrett Zecker is the publisher and co-founder of Quabbin Quills. He holds an MA in English from Fitchburg State University and an MFA in Fiction from Southern New Hampshire University's Mountainview MFA. He founded Perpetual Imagination in 2004, specializing in independent releases and live events. Garrett is a writer, actor, and teacher of writing and literature. Links to his work, including other publications, full Shakespeare In The Park performances, and hundreds of book and movie reviews can be found at his blog,
GarrettZecker.com.

ABOUT OUR EDITORS

Author **Diane Kane's** fiction and nonfiction short stories appear in Red Penguin, Monadnock Underground, and Written Tales publications. She is one of the founding members of Quabbin Quills and continues to be closely involved in the nonprofit organization. Kane is the publisher and co-author of *Flash in the Can Number One* and *Number Two*, books of short stories. She also writes public interest articles for *Uniquely Quabbin Magazine* and several newspapers. Kane's first children's book, *Don Gateau the Three-Legged Cat of Seborga*, published in English, Spanish, French and Italian, won the Purple Dragonfly Award for Caring/Making a Difference in 2020. The sequel, *Don Gateau Moves to Vallebona*, is due for publication in 2023. Kane published her second children's book, *Brayden the Brave Goes to* *the Hospital*, in April 2021 with the endorsement of Boston Children's Hospital. Look for her first novel, *I Never Called Him Pa* published this year. Follow her on Facebook @PageofPossibilities

James Thibeault is the Treasurer of Quabbin Quills and is proud to have served on the board for all of these years. His previous publications include two young adult novels, *Deacon's Folly* and *Michael's Black Dress*, as well as a children's book, *Melanie and the Box.* He is currently a librarian at Quinebaug Valley Community College.

Karen Traub holds an MFA from Salve Regina University in Newport, RI. Her poetry and creative nonfiction have been published in *Brevity Magazine, Straw Dog Writer's Guild Pandemic Poetry and Prose*, and *Quabbin Quills* anthologies. Karen lives in Shutesbury, MA with her husband Frank, and her royal python Chloe.

Fred Gerhard is one of the founders of the New Dawn Writers' Group in Ashburnham where he leads monthly poetry workshops. He was the editor of *The Chelmsford Poetry Review* and is an editor at Quabbin Quills. His poems have appeared in *Amethyst Review, Asylum Magazine, Black Moon Magazine, Contemporary Dance, Entropy Magazine, The Friends Journal, Harpy Hybrid Review, Heavy Feather Review, Monadnock Underground, Pif Magazine, POETiCA REViEW, Sylvia Magazine, Wild Musette Journal*, and other magazines and anthologies. His life calling is to encourage writers, and to be a kind human being.

David Barry is a psychotherapist who writes genre fiction. He hails from Worcester, Massachusetts, where he spends his leisure time with his life partner, her daughter, their dog Lola, and a cat named Mouse. You can follow David (and Lola) on Twitter at @DavidMBarry.

Sharon A. Harmon is a poet and freelance writer. Her chapbooks are *Swimming with Cats* and *Wishbone in a Lightning Jar.* She is the author of two children's books. She has published over 300 poems and also writes for magazines and anthologies. She has been published twice in *Chicken Soup for the Soul*, as well as *Taste of Home, Birds and Blooms* and *Highlights for Children.* Her poetry has appeared in *The Patterson Literary Review*, *Writing the Land Northeast,* and *Compass Roads.* Sharon has taught workshops for writing poetry, memoir, and writing for magazines. Find her on Facebook at Sharon A. Harmon Poet & Writer and also Sharon Ann Harmon Publishing.

Cecilia Januszewski is a senior at Reed College in Portland, Oregon, where she studies linguistic anthropology and spends all her free time reading, going for walks, and admiring other people's dogs. She is currently editing the manuscript of her first novel and has been previously published in Blue Marble Review, Quibble, Manuscripts, and Quabbin Quills, where she is now an editorial board member.

Charlotte Taylor has published short stories and poetry and hoards a collection of unedited novels. She loves the process of creating characters, stories, and worlds. Charlotte is an active blogger for her work in Ayurveda and yoga. She is actively seeking a life of peace, study, and fun. Charlotte can often be found surrounded by cats with a mug of tea and reading books. Other times, you'll find her practicing yoga, climbing mountains, and sometimes crawling under barbed wire.

Michael Young is the current Poet Laureate for Royalston, MA. His work has appeared in three former Quabbin Quills anthologies as well as *Uniquely Quabbin Magazine, Trout, Grit*, and *A Time for Singing*. Currently he is working on his memoir, *Playing in the Weeds*. An Adult Education instructor in creative writing at MWCC (The Mount), two of his students have pieces in *Beyond the Pathway*. Michael enjoys fly fishing when not writing or working with his wife, Pat, on their Greenfyre Farm. His weekly *Universal Meditation* show may be heard on WVAO-FM.

OUR SCHOLARSHIP AND STUDENT CONTRIBUTORS

Skylar Winn is an 18 year old girl from a small town in Massachusetts. She attends Murdock High School and will be graduating in May. Skylar loves reading, art, riding horses, and working hard to achieve her goals. After she graduates she plans to work for her dreams and continue to write and even possibly publish a book.

Olly Lefsyk is 14 years old in 8th grade and has always found any sort of writing beautiful in the way words can be used to capture emotions. In the author's own words: "For that reason exactly, I found joy in writing as a way to express the feelings I do not quite understand. I'm not sure if I can call what I write poetry because it's just my emotions mixed in with fun, pretty words I like and used to try to explain them."

Sophia Januszewski is a young artist. She has been published previously in Art on the Trails Exposure with special mention. She enjoys painting, drawing, and writing.

Jayden Lindsay is a student at Murdock high school who currently has no previous publications but has a lot of writing experience via school and personal work. She loves writing poetry, stories, reading, and drawing. She is an only child and has two dogs, she also moved from a different state the summer of freshman year.

Donovan M. Whitaker's hobby with music, passion for poetry, experience in media, admiration for cinema, reverie mind, and absurdist values all culminate into his zeal for creative expression and experimentation. Donovan's creative drive, as he puts it: "yearn to and shall be a bold face in the crowd of gold."

Curly Rae has not been previously published, but has been creating artistic works most of their life. Their work and life is very inspired by hip hop, classic literature, and philosophy. They are an English Major at Quinebaug Valley Community College.

ABOUT OUR CONTRIBUTORS

Alison Clark is an aspiring poet who enjoys writing in her free time. Her main inspirations are nature, sunsets, and often the moon. She has been published in one previous Quabbin Quills anthology.

Allan Fournier is a retired software engineer who has always enjoyed working with words. He enjoys sharing his poems at local poetry and open mic nights, and appeared in the *Beyond the Pathway* Quabbin Quills anthology, along with a couple of other local anthologies. He was honored to recite poems related to his father's recent death from lymphoma at the Spring 2022 Attleboro Area "Slam Cancer" and "Relay For Life" events. He has started work on his first book of poems and related stories. Notes about his writing: "The Wind" is a true story about a track workout in college.

Amanda Russell is a poet and stay-at-home mom. Her chapbook, *Barren Years*, was published by Finishing Line Press (2019). Her poems have appeared or are forthcoming in *The Jarnal Vol. 3, First Literary Review- East, EcoTheo Review, South Florida Poetry Journa*l and the anthology *Mightier: Poets for Social Justice*. For links to poems, interviews and more, please visit https://poetrussell.wordpress.com.

Annette Ermini lives in scenic Petersham, MA with her husband, Jim, and their two beloved cats. Together they own a real estate agency, New England Classic Homes, and Annette serves the community as a Select Person and Library Trustee. She enjoys writing about wellness, including topics related to the mind, body, and spirit. She can be reached at www.neclassichomes.com.

Aurynanya lives and writes in the North Quabbin region of Massachusetts. She writes beautifully dark and devastating poetry that invokes the raw, the honest, and the beautifully tragic. When not busy creating, Aury enjoys immersing herself in poetry, graphic design, art, mental health advocacy, thriller/horror novels, movies, and music (especially lyrics). She also happens to be owned by two spoiled black cats.

Barbara Vosburgh is a second time Quabbin Quills author. In the past, she has been a news reporter and feature writer. She has also published humor and gardening articles. Today she is happily retired in Fitchburg filling her time with writing, crafts, gardening, knitting, learning new skills, and news. Her greatest joy is watching her youngest grandchild grow and spending time with him. Barbara feeds her wild critters every day. Some of the squirrels and chipmunks eat out of her hand. Each critter has a name, including the rabbits, turkey, opossum, and birds. She says she is proud to be among such talented writers.

Dr. Ben Fine was a mathematician and professor at Fairfield University in Connecticut in the United States. He was a graduate of the MFA program at Fairfield University and the author of twelve books (ten in mathematics, one on chess, one a political thriller) as well over 130 research articles. In addition he published several short stories as well as a novella about pirates. His memoir, told in interwoven stories is *Tales from Brighton Beach: A Boy Grows in Brooklyn* and it details growing up during the 1950's and 1960'si n Brighton Beach, a seaside neighborhood on the southern tip of Brooklyn. Brighton Beach was unique and set apart from the rest of New York City both in character and in time. He passed away in March of 2023 and we are honored to publish his final work.

Carlene M. Gadapee lives and teaches English in northern New Hampshire, and she is the Associate Creative Director for The Frost Place Studio Sessions in Franconia. Her work has been published in a variety of journals, among them *Waterwheel Review, Smoky Quartz, Margate Bookie, Bloodroot*, and *Gyroscope Review*. Carlene resides with her husband in Littleton.

Chele Pedersen Smith lives in Ashburnham, Massachusetts with her husband Bob, and their feisty golden retriever, Penny, who loves sniffing into the wind— her own "information superhighway." When Chele (short for Michele) is not residing in her fictional world, she is a pharmacy technician at Hannaford and a mom to two grown kids. A self-proclaimed "word nerd," she began writing in sixth grade and took all the English/writing electives in high school and college. Besides having a spiritual short published in *Guideposts* in 2019, Chele is thrilled to have stories in Quabbin Quill's anthologies, beginning with *Beyond the Pathway* in 2021 and last year's *Cascades and Currents.* Her published books can be found on Amazon and other retailers and include *Behind Frenemy Lines* (a spy romance), *The Epochracy Files* (a collection of time-twisting tales) real mini miracles in *The Pearly Gates Phone Company*, the futuristic and retro mystery, *Chronicle of the Century*, *Parlor Game* (a dragon and wizard quest), and three Christmas/winter holiday books: *Snow Angels, the Peppermint Bark Olympics*, and *Apartment Door Santa.*

David Story Allen has sailed on lakes and off New England for a number of years. He has taught in the humanities at independent schools in the United States as well as in East Asia. David has degrees from Syracuse, the University of New Hampshire and Harvard. His novel *Off Tom Nevers*, set at a New England boarding school, was published in 2017. He recently completed a nonfiction book on two murders that occurred years ago in New Hampshire, where he currently teaches and sails.

Diana Tamulevich lives in a small town in Massachusetts. She recently completed her BA in English and Creative Writing and is excited to pursue her dream of creating young adult fiction stories and continuing writing poetry about life's adventures. She has four grown children and one grandson who she adores. She lives with her "Aspy" husband and a myriad of furry family members. She enjoys camping, crafting, and gardening but her true passion is writing.

Diane Hinckley is a mostly retired copy editor, living in the North Quabbin Region, to which she returned after decades of living and working in other parts of the Commonwealth. She enjoys writing fiction and indulging in an occasional travel adventure. Her story "Ice" incorporates names from Diane Hinckley's genealogy, a visit to a Civil War battlefield where Central Massachusetts farmers fought in the Louisiana heat, and impressions from classical Greek literature.

Ed Londergan has been writing part-time for years. One fine April day in 2016, he quit his job and began writing full-time. He realized that if not then, when? Taking a great leap of faith in himself, he worked as a freelance writer for five years. Realizing time waits for no one, he decided to focus his energies on writing books, so he closed the business. He now writes what he wants to when he wants to. He believes that it's not work if you enjoy it. Each of his three books has won awards from the New England Book Festival. Five years ago, he co-founded the Quaboag Writers Collaborative, a writer's group that provides honest, unflinching critiques of members' work. Ed, and his fellow QWC members, believe it is one of the best ways to become a better writer. He teaches an annual creative writing workshop and speaks throughout the area on writing and history topics.

Ed Ahern resumed writing after forty odd years in foreign intelligence and international sales. He's had 450 stories and poems published so far, and six books. Ed works the other side of writing at Bewildering Stories, where he manages a posse of eight review editors. He's also lead editor at *The Scribes Micro Fiction* magazine

Ellie Burton is a multi-genre romance author and poet who has lived in Massachusetts all her life. Her first poetry collection, *A Pocket Full of Wildflowers*, has maintained a 5-star rating. Ellie was also selected to participate in *Eber & Wein Publishing's Best Poets of 2022* as well as multiple other anthologies. She holds a BA in Creative Writing and English from Southern New Hampshire University and an AA in Professional Writing and AS in IDS from Mount Wachusett Community College. When Ellie is not busy writing, you can find her reading, painting, or spending time with her husband and sons. Keep in touch with Ellie via Instagram @ellie.burton_author.

Emelie Rutherford is a high school English teacher and former print journalist.

Heidi Larsen is a 4th Grade teacher at a small Christian Academy in Central Massachusetts. She is a storyteller and writer at heart, who uses her Masters in Education to make words come to life. Heidi met her husband-to-be, Larry Larsen, in a small "puddle jumper" airplane in Seattle, Washington. Little did they know that they would walk across the tarmac and into each other's lives. Together they're parents to Holden and Cooper, who have been their greatest and most satisfying adventure so far. Outside of the classroom, you may find Heidi cozying up to a cup of Chai Tea, reading her favorite historical fiction, or searching for God's hearts in nature as signs of His love.

John Grey is an Australian poet, US resident, recently published in Stand, Washington Square Review and Floyd County Moonshine. His latest books, *Covert, Memory Outside The Head,* and *Guest Of Myself* are available through Amazon. His upcoming work can also be seen in the *McNeese Review, Santa Fe Literary Review* and *Open Ceilings.*

Judith O'Connell Hoyer's chapbook, *Bits and Pieces Set Aside* was nominated for a Massachusetts Book Award by the publisher of Finishing Line Press. Her first full-length poetry collection, *Imagine*

That was published in February 2023 by FutureCycle Press. Poems by her have appeared in journals that include, *Atlanta Review, CALYX Magazine, Cider Press Review, Southwest Review, Tar River Review, The Moth Magazine* (Ireland) and *The Worcester Review.*

Although **Justine Johnston Hemmestad** lives in Iowa, she very much wanted her story, which is centered around Edgar Allan Poe and takes place in New England, included in this anthology. Justine is included in several anthologies, including *Chicken Soup for the Soul: Recovering from Traumatic Brain Injuries.* She sustained a brain injury at nineteen years old, and went on to write three novels. She is a graduate of The University of Iowa along with graduating from the English Literature Master's Degree program with distinction at Northern Arizona University. Her story, "My Beating Heart," was previously published in *Forgotten Horrors* (Fae Shivers) in 2021.

Karen E. Wagner, a physicist, writes poetry as a retirement vocation. Her work appears in the *Quabbin Quills Anthology 2022*, in the *Goose River Anthology* each year since 2016, in the *BOLLI Journal* for six years until its final issue in 2019-20. She enjoys wordsmithing and expression of concepts beyond the realm of logic. Karen lives in Hudson, MA with her cat, Star.

Kathy Bennett's poetry has appeared in several anthologies, including internationally, in the past 20 years. Her favorite place to submit, however, is for the Quabbin Quills publications (three years consecutively). Much of her poetic inspiration has come from the Quabbin region before she moved from Templeton to the city of Taunton. Quabbin provides the perfect area for creating and recreating, something not experienced in her new surroundings.

Kathryn Chaisson's earliest memory as a writer is when she created a story in first grade about a talking skunk. As an adult, her writing has been featured in numerous local newspapers and various other publications.

Kathy Chencharik is a freelance writer and has been published in several newspapers, magazines, and anthologies. She won the Derringer Award for best flash fiction for her short story "The Book

Signing " in *Thin Ice* (a Level Best Books anthology, 2010). She earned numerous honorable mentions for her stories in *Alfred Hitchcock's Mystery Magazine*'s Mysterious Photograph contest. Her story "the Widow " finally won the prize in the November/December 2020 issue of the magazine.

Kersti Slowik is a born and bred New Englander who lives outside of Boston with her husband and daughter. She enjoys writing poetry for friends and family every holiday season. Her work was also included in the Quabbin Quills anthology *Cascades and Currents.*

Lauren Elise Fisher is a Connecticut based theatre artist/stage manager. She holds a B.A. in theatre studies from the University of Connecticut where she studied stage management, performance, and puppet arts—all experiences she is incredibly thankful for. When she isn't working with a stage or a pen, you'll probably find her pulling her hair out over a tarot spread. Keep up with Lauren on Instagram: @AllFishSwim.

Les Clark is the author of three books (one each: fiction, nonfiction, and humor) and a previous contributor to Quabbin Quills *Beyond the Pathway.* Even though he is a retiree, he puts in three days a week working for Staples. Les is a graduate of Northeastern University earning, after 17 years at night, two degrees in business. In his off hours, he and his fiancé cook and spend time in Rhode Island. Les is an Air Force veteran who violated the code and volunteered for everything.

Lorri Ventura is a retired special education administrator living in Massachusetts. Her writing has been featured in a number of anthologies, and she is a three-time winner of the Moon Prize for poetry.

An accountant by education and trade, **LuAnn Thibodeau** discovered that there is a creative side to her brain. She was previously published in the last Quabbin Quills anthology, and has also had articles published in *The Medford Transcript, The Suburban Newspaper* in Quebec, and in *Worcester Pulse Magazine.*

Mackenzie Lafreniere is a 17 year old student at Murdock High School. She has many hobbies such as drawing, painting, reading, and her personal favorite: writing. She has grown up being complimented on both her artistic and creative writing skills. Kenzie has been drawing and writing her whole life. She has won first place in a poetry contest, and works hard to be the best she can. She hopes that one day she can write her own poetry book or novel to share her story with the world. Along with wanting to study law in college, Kenzie has many goals in life that she knows she can accomplish.

Mackenzie Scanlon is an aspiring writer. She graduated with a Bachelor's degree in Business Management from Bridgewater State University. Mackenzie resides in Massachusetts with her husband and their dog, Charlie.

Marilynn Carter is a holistic health practitioner, teacher and life coach at Many Paths for Health, the co-owner of Maat Publishing; and author of two books, *No Fret Cooking*, and *Experience the Love Light Wisdom of Reiki.* Her poetry has appeared in *Trouvaille Review; the Merrimac Mic Anthology II: Going with the Floes; Lunation, A Good Fat Anthology of 114 Women Poets*; and *Klarissa Dreams Redux: The Illuminated Anthology*; at the Methuen Arts outdoor poetry installation, *Words by Winter Waterfall*; and *Word Play*, a virtual exhibit of poetic art. Her first chapbook of poetry was published in 2021.

Mark Schafron's stories have appeared in *Atom Mind, American Epitaph, Fiction Forum*, and *Chips off the Writer's Block*, among others. His non-fiction and journalism have appeared nationally in a number of technical journals and periodicals.

MJ LaCroix writes essays, creative nonfiction, and children's books. Her love of writing and books began with winning a spelling bee in elementary school. The prize, one of the Nancy Drew mystery series, instilled a natural curiosity about mystery and illusion. Still drawn to wild places, LaCroix resides in north central Massachusetts. LaCroix was recently published in the last issue of Quabbin Quills Anthology, *Cascades and Currents.*

Mary Anne Slack is a writer and freelance editor living in Central

Massachusetts. Her short stories have been published in *MUSED* and in *Adelaide Literary Magazine*. She is a member of the Quaboag Writers Collaborative.

Mary J. Kellar has been writing since she was fourteen. She has a poetry book *Sketches of Life* (1985). Mary has written short stories, articles, and cookbooks. She has published pieces in several newspapers and the magazine's *Ideals, Bittersweet, True Confessions* and poetry and stories in *A Patchwork Christmas,* an anthology. She is a long-standing member of the Central Mass Writers Group. She lives with her son in Winchendon.

Melissa D. Burrage is a historian and author of *The Karl Muck Scandal: Classical Music and Xenophobia in World War 1 America* She began writing poetry in earnest after her twenty-two-year-old son died in a tragic motorcycle accident in his final semester of college. She is a member of the Westwood Poetry Group, the Marge Piercy Poetry Group, and a 2022 winner of the Joe Gouveia Outermost Poetry Contest. Her work can be found in *Portrait of New England Magazine, Persimmon Tree, Libretto Magazine, Paterson Literary Review, Duality, Quillkeepers Press, Poetica Review, Foyer Magazine, Syncopation Literary Journal, Sweetycat Press, Dashboard Horus, Smoky Quartz Tenth Anniversary Literary Anthology, Southern Arizona Press: The Poppy: A Symbol of Remembrance Anthology* and *Cephalopress: Border and Belonging Anthology.* Visit melissadburrage.com for more information.

Melissa Dorval's debut novel, *WHEN YOU LOSE CONTROL*, (Spinning Monkey Press) is coming summer 2023. Dorval's works have been published in *The Offering, The Lowell Connector, The Sixpence Society Literary Journal*, and *The Creative Zine.* In 2009, Dorval graduated magna cum laude from UMass, where best-selling author, Andre Dubus III, was her mentor.

Molly Chambers has lived in New England since 1970. She moved to Western Massachusetts in 1973. She has worked as a teacher and social worker for over 37 years. Molly received her B.A. in sociology-Anthropology from Antioch College and her M.Ed from the University of Massachusetts at Amherst. Molly's two adult children are also poets and is most likely attributed to Molly's mother who was also a poet.

Nelson Linscott has lived a varied life that some would consider exciting. He is an amateur photographer and storyteller. Linscott has lived most of his life in Kittery, Maine. Although he left a few times, he always returned. Linscott lives with his beloved shelter dog, Luna, who came from Puerto Rico.

Nicole LaChance is a gifted artist who lives in Sterling and captured a striking photo of a simple flower garden in Virginia at Colonial Williamsburg many years back. Her dear friend Kathleen Bennet asked if she could use that piece to go along with the poem Kathleen submitted for this anthology. Nicole was honored to do so.

Phyllis Cochran has been a published writer since 1990. Her inspirational stories have appeared in *Woman's World, Focus on the Family, Good Old Days, Chicken Soup for the Soul*, and other magazines, newspapers and books. After a difficult year, Phyllis continues to write from the heart. She also spends time teaching great-grandchildren to write, knit and sew. Her children's picture book, *Whose Cat is That?* was published in 2020.

R.S. Fox is a writer, presently writing in but not originally from New England. Most of the details of his story are true. R.S. Fox can be contacted at rsfoxrsfoxrsfox@gmail.com

Shali Sanders continues to appreciate the written word, the drawing, painting and creativity of all who can impact life with vision and clarity. She has had the great honor of being a local medical provider for over 30 years as an OB/GYNP and as the carrier of artistic expression from her Father. Poetry frequently fills her, as does the inescapable vantage point of art as life presents itself. Shali is honored to share her view.

Sue Moreines is a retired child psychologist who now has time to focus on writing about various struggles and overcoming adversity. Always seeking to pay-it-forward, Sue and her rescue dog Daisy volunteer at the library to allow young children the opportunity to practice reading and to enjoy the benefits of pet therapy.

Tom Anthony currently lives in York, Maine. He is a veteran who also pursued a long time career in college admissions. His writing started with poetry over fifty years ago and continues today with essays, biography, and fiction. His other interests include woodcarving and furniture building, and for most of his life, he has been an eager singer and occasional actor. Among his most notable accomplishments, he ran the New York Marathon in 1979.

Tricia Knoll is a Vermont poet who admires the wind turbines down the road, watches when they turn and how fast. She has long hair and enjoys the feel of a stout wind blowing through it. Her work appears widely in journals and anthologies. She is a Contributing Editor to *Verse Virtual.* In 2023, her latest collections are: *One Bent Twig* from Future Cycle Press and *Wild Apples* from Fernwood Press in summer. Both books rely on her life in a bit of land in Vermont. Visit her website: triciaknoll.com.

Tulip Chowdhury is an educationalist and writer who loves connecting to nature. She has authored several books, including her novel, *Visible, Invisible and Beyond* and a poetry collection, *Red, Blue, and Purple*, along with her latest book, *Soul Inside Out.* The books are available on Amazon/Kindle and at Barnes and Noble. Tulip writes from Massachusetts.

William Doreski lives in Peterborough, New Hampshire. He has taught at several colleges and universities. His most recent book of poetry is *Dogs Don't Care* (2022). His essays, poetry, fiction, and reviews have appeared in various journals.

Support Our Local Sponsors!

Printing yearly anthologies isn't cheap.

Fortunately, Quabbin Quills has some amazing local sponsors to help with our production costs.

Please consider reaching out and supporting them!

This Quabbin Quills Anthology has been brought to you by the following generous sponsors…

Porter Transportation.
Sand - Gravel - Stone - Loam
978-575-0567

FISHER
https://fishertechsolutions.com
efisher@fishertechsolutions.com
WEBSITE TROUBLE?
Increase Traffic, Conversions
and Functionality With
Fisher Tech Solutions LLC

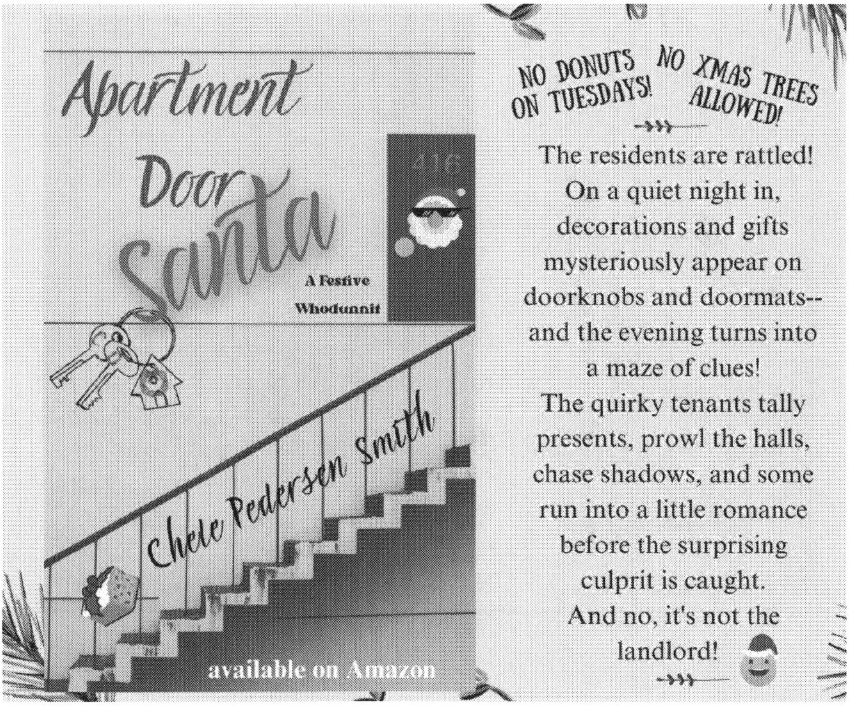

Carpe

You may not write well every day, but you can always edit a bad page.

YOU CAN'T EDIT A BLANK PAGE

—

Jodi Picoult

Librum

Red Apple Farm in Phillipston, MA, has been running since 1912, owned by the Rose family for over 4 generations. We started as a wholesaler to local stores then converted to a Pick Your Own destination open to the public.

Find us online at RedAppleFarm.com and @redapplefarm on Facebook

We provide an Authentic New England Family Farm Experience and celebrate Fall all year long.

From our Ski Season at Bullock Lodge on Wachusett Mountain, to Blueberries then Sunflowers in the summer, to Apples, Pumpkins, Potatoes and more in the Fall until our Harvest Festival, and then our Winter Lights walk through the orchards. We now make our own Hard Cider, available in the Brew Barn restaurant on site and for purchase to go.

Our store is open every day, with our Yankee Magazine award winning Cider Donuts, a quintessential New England treat!

please consider making a donation to
Uniquely Quabbin magazine
with a check to
Uniquely Quabbin c/o Debra Ellis,business manager
1390 Chestnut Hill Avenue • Athol, MA 01331
THANK YOU!

Uniquely Quabbin magazine

gratefully acknowledges the support of

Athol Cultural Council • Barre Cultural Council • Brookfield Cultural Council
Hardwick-New Braintree Cultural Council • Hubbardston Cultural Council • New Salem Cultural Council
North Brookfield Cultural Council • Oakham Cultural Council • Orange Cultural Council
Pelham Cultural Council • Petersham Cultural Council • Phillipston Cultural Council
Royalston Cultural Council • Templeton Cultural Council • Ware Cultural Council
Warwick Cultural Council • Wendell Cultural Council• West Brookfield Cultural Council

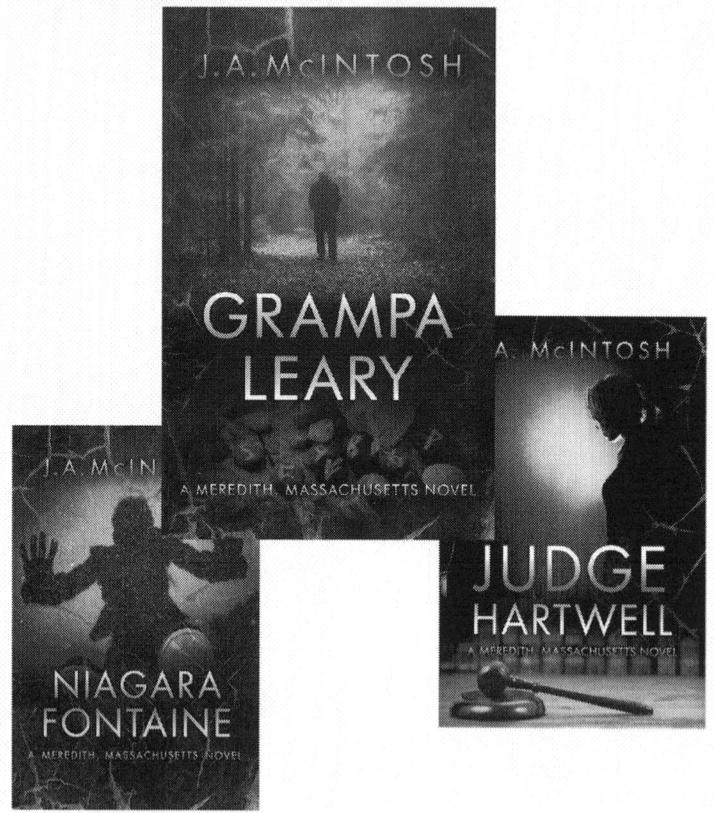
J.A.McINTOSH
GRAMPA
LEARY
A MEREDITH, MASSACHUSETTS NOVEL
JUDGE
HARTWELL
A MEREDITH, MASSACHUSETTS NOVEL
NIAGARA
FONTAINE
A MEREDITH, MASSACHUSETTS NOVEL

**Check out
other books by
Clare Green**

www.claregreenbooks.com

Warmer Winters is a group that provides hand-made hats, mittens, scarves, and sweaters. It is an all-volunteer organization that began 17 years ago, when one woman saw the need of a young mother and her children, while waiting for a bus in Leominster. That began the organization, which has given over 30,000 hand crafted articles of warmth, as neighbors helping neighbors.

Warmer Winters, a 501c3 organization
www.warmerwinters.org

Made in the USA
Columbia, SC
21 October 2023